THE TIMES
CROSSWORD

BOOK 5

**Selected and introduced by
Mike Laws**

**Originally edited by
Brian Greer or Mike Laws**

TIMES BOOKS

Published in 2002 by Times Books

HarperCollins*Publishers*
77-85 Fulham Palace Road
Hammersmith
London W6 8JB

www.harpercollins.co.uk
Visit the book lover's website

Reprint 10 9 8 7 6 5 4 3 2 1

The Times is a registered trademark of
Times Newspapers Ltd

ISBN 0-00-714496-2

British Library Cataloguing in Publication Data
A catalogue record for this book is available from the British Library.

Thank you to David Akenhead and Jennifer Baird for proof correcting.

Typeset in Great Britain by Davidson Pre-Press Graphics Ltd, Glasgow G3

Printed and bound by Thomson Press (India) Ltd

INTRODUCTION

"I would like to compile crosswords for *The Times*..." begins an enquiring letter. How realistic is this ambition?

Currently there are ten regular compilers, each contributing between one and four crosswords a month, and a lengthy list of occasionals, all of whom have proved their mettle. The regulars are guaranteed their frequencies until they decide to retire, or let their standards slip. The queue of occasionals can be joined, but it cannot be jumped by sheer confidence or optimism – some experience is a *sine qua non*.

"I have been a *Times* solver for many years..." Unfortunately, expertise in solving them does not guarantee skill at composing clues, especially for *The Times*. Many of the sharpest solvers unravel the cryptic implications of a clue so quickly that the effort put into making it grammatically sound, and read like a more or less sensible piece of prose, is all but lost on them.

"I enclose a sample of my work..." is more promising, but only if the sample, whether or not it has been published elsewhere, demonstrates a basic understanding of the general principles of crossword compiling, and particular evidence of sympathy with the *Times* style.

"I appreciate the value of a crossword which needs little or no editing..." in one covering letter impressed John Grant (Crossword Editor 1983–95). The writer had studied and analysed which techniques were used in *The Times* Crossword, but just as importantly, noted those which weren't. John said the puzzle was better than those of some of his longer-term contributors, but he couldn't bring himself to put them out to grass just yet, and occasional gaps occurred only rarely – about three times a year, as it turned out.

The ambition is realistic only if accompanied by the appropriate skill, willingness to adapt, a lot of patience – and perhaps a little bit of luck!

This book covers the second half of 2000. Among the 34 puzzles originally edited by Brian Greer are all those used in *The Times* Crossword Championships that year. His references to the change of editorship are hidden in the solutions to puzzles 28 (horizontally) and 43 (diagonally).

Mike Laws
Crossword Editor of *The Times*
October 2002

A BEGINNER'S GUIDE TO *THE TIMES* CROSSWORD

ACROSS

1 High-flier ruined by exposure in Sun (6)
5 Nonconformist churchman's back I protected from rain (8)
9 Opposition is hesitant to reform (10)
10 Arranger selecting odd pieces for composer (4)
11 Frosty spell in unfriendly game (4,4)
12 Characteristic tone in old instrument cut short (6)
13 Charge for conversion as gas is offered, initially (4)
15 Call artist a venomous creature (8)
18 Strange sort of small house? Indeed, it was (8)
19 Absence of authorisation for retreat (4)
21 Was mistress under stress? Sounds like it (6)
23 Specify drink – same again? (8)
25 Architect leaves sewer after fall (4)
26 Like a resistance force made up without ringleader (10)
27 American statesman noted for his Canterbury relation (8)
28 For example, miss a run (6)

DOWN

2 Censor accepts new section in poem (5)
3 They make up shower curtains artist at home put up (9)
4 "A man" finally solved her cryptic puzzle (6)
5 Maiden is under arrest? Just the opposite – that's an error (15)
6 One making late appearance (it's in a TV broadcast) (8)
7 Raise millions to modernise the forces (5)
8 Singer, no pro, gets lot wrong (9)
14 One sort of bird – and another right outside (9)
16 Leaves without the slightest difficulty (5,4)
17 Small meal? It's hard to say (8)
20 Fine Italian instruments you love in Rome (6)
22 Involved in begging, a minor? (5)
24 One in exaltation turned up round a village (5)

NOTES
ACROSS

1 ICARUS The whole clue is a cryptic definition and has nothing to do with a tabloid scandal about a successful person. Icarus and his father, Daedalus, made wings to escape from Crete, but Icarus flew too high and the wax securing his wings melted in the sun's rays, so he fell to his death.

4

5 MAVERICK = nonconformist. The rest works like an algebraic equation, thus: VER (= churchman's back) + I inside MACK (i.e. protected from rain).

9 ANTITHESIS = opposition. Anagram of IS HESITANT (indicator: to reform).

10 ARNE = composer (Thomas Arne, 1710–1778). More unusual clue type instructing solver to select odd letters (pieces) of ArRaNgEr.

11 COLD SNAP = frosty spell. Combination of COLD (= unfriendly) + SNAP (= game).

12 TIMBRE = characteristic tone. Timbrel (old instrument) is cut short.

13 AGIO = charge for conversion (when changing money). First letters (indicator: initially) of As Gas Is Offered.

15 RINGHALS = a venomous creature (large spitting cobra). Combination of RING (call) + HALS (artist).

18 FORSOOTH = indeed (note that "it was" points to the word being archaic).
Anagram: SORT OF HO (ho. = small house, i.e. abbreviation) (indicator:
strange).

19 NOOK = retreat. Absence of authorisation = NO OK.

21 TAUGHT = was mistress. Homophone of taut = under stress (indicator:
sounds like it).

23 NAMESAKE = same again (somewhat cryptic definition signalled by question
mark). Combination of NAME (specify) + SAKE (drink).

25 Two definitions. ADAM = architect/ADAM = leaves sewer after fall (Adam
and Eve sewed fig-leaves to make aprons).

26 FRICTIONAL = like a resistance force. FICTIONAL (= made up) outside
(without) R (= ringleader).

27 Two definitions. FRANKLIN = American statesman (Benjamin Franklin,
1706–1790) FRANKLIN = noted for his Canterbury relation. ("Franklin's
Tale" is one of *The Canterbury Tales*).

28 Two definitions. SINGLE = for example, miss (i.e. an unmarried
person)/SINGLE = a run.

DOWN

2 CANTO = section in poem. CATO = censor (Marcus Porcius Cato, elected
censor in 184, famous for his zeal in that capacity), contains (accepts) N = new.

3 RAINDROPS = they make up shower. DROPS = curtains, with RA (= artist)
+ IN (= at home) on top (put up).

4 The whole clue is a cryptic definition. The SPHINX was a female monster
inhabiting the district around Thebes, who set the riddle, "What animal
walks on four legs in the morning, two at noon, and three in the evening?"
Oedipus finally provided the answer, "A man", who crawls as a baby, walks
upright in mid-life and with the aid of a stick in old age.

5 MISAPPREHENSION = an error. M (= maiden) + IS on top of (under?
Just the opposite) APPREHENSION (= arrest).

6 VISITANT = one making late appearance (a visitant is a ghost, i.e. late =
dead person). Anagram: IT'S IN A TV (indicator: broadcast).

7 REARM = modernise the forces. Combination of REAR (= raise) +
M (= millions, abbreviation).

8 CONTRALTO = singer. Combination of CONTRA (= no pro) + anagram of
LOT (indicator: wrong).

14 GOOSANDER = one sort of bird. AND with GOOSE (= another (bird)) +
R (= right, abbreviation) outside.

16 Two definitions. HANDS DOWN = leaves (i.e. bequeaths)/HANDS DOWN
= without the slightest difficulty.

6

17 Two definitions. MOUTHFUL = small meal/MOUTHFUL = it's hard to say.

20 Two definitions. AMATIS = fine Italian instruments (plural of Amati)/AMATIS = you love in Rome (amo, amas, amat, amamus, amatis …)

22 The whole clue acts both as a definition (GAMIN is a street urchin who might be involved in begging) and hidden clue – begginG A MINor (indicator: involved in).

24 KRAAL = village. LARK (= one in exaltation, exaltation being the collective noun for larks) inverted (turned up), containing (round) A.

THE PUZZLES

1

ACROSS

1 Underworld bosses moving East (5)
4 Gallery where one feels at home? (9)
9 It charts country's rise and fall (6,3)
10 Book featured in *The Times* about old horse-soldier (5)
11 Ejected, knowing how to be a better pilot? (6)
12 Author's sound description of father (8)
14 Fair target (9)
16 Old mass included in musical performance in European cathedral (5)
17 A bit of culture (5)
19 Rejected plan to introduce English ways into foreign islands (9)
21 Settling elsewhere's an awful nightmare without husband (8)
22 Man, perhaps, I fully extended (6)
25 Surrealist recalled penning one long poem (5)
26 Star signs to provide this (9)
27 Capital leader transformed old army soldiers (4,5)
28 Territory in Canada that includes our state (5)

DOWN

1 London borough offering good prospects for schoolboys? (6-2-3-4)
2 Was first to set up newspaper in China (5)
3 Once a record defeat for the US (7)
4 Familiar ingredient of Spanish omelette (4)
5 Carried by rifleman into bank, from what we hear (10)
6 As a deputy, detains crook (7)
7 Outstanding score at golf resulting in handicap (9)
8 The navy renowned at sea? Not always (5,3,3,4)
13 Like colour of pitman, grey after shift (10)
15 Apologist? Only if that's right (9)
18 Ordeal that's shaken military leader in high office (7)
20 Happy with bill for bunch of flowers (7)
23 One thing that's missing, unfortunately (5)
24 Mix thoroughly in jug or can (4)

2

ACROSS

1 He helps others cope with the ups and downs of navigation (4-6)
6 It shows the pitch's cracked, unfinished (4)
9 One makes a hole for each loudspeaker (10)
10 Within three, four, or five, one or two (4)
12 Broken sculpture (4)
13 Bankrupt at home getting thinner (9)
15 Moral instructions for rate collections (8)
16 Group of gamblers in coach (6)
18 Frequent recreation area (6)
20 Small swimmers – little perches (8)
23 His home is left on the map (9)
24 Prints produced by experts (4)
26 Name old bird initially as grouse (4)
27 Destroyer made for the docks, for example (10)
28 Boat-builder located in Genoa harbour (4)
29 Sort of pencil mate used with chart (10)

DOWN

1 Bound to name Spanish dramatist (4)
2 Within reason, men turned up to drink freely (7)
3 Broadcasting networks hope to be expert (5,3,5)
4 Make very thin English china foreign agents imported (8)
5 One whose trips are image-building (6)
7 Plain man writing lines on a tyrant (7)
8 Like post needed asap in kindergarten (5-5)
11 Boycott stupid person's meat product (5,7)
14 She's specially suited for long-distance travel (10)
17 Fierce old girl tormented, we hear, a nervous head (8)
19 Cosmetic mother used to cover a blemish (7)
21 High court action by author is a bloomer (7)
22 Men she contrived to catch (6)
25 Knowing chief at the start and ruler at the end (4)

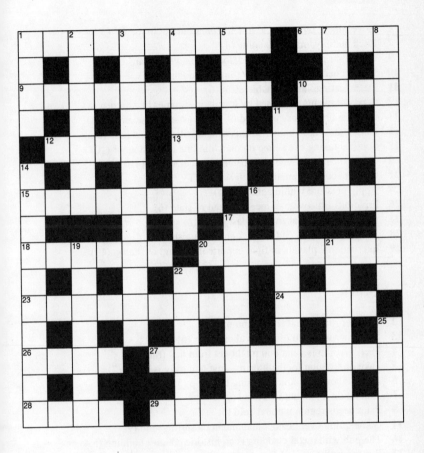

3

ACROSS

1 Government report found in *The Times* but not in the *FT* (5,5)
7 Pitch audibly, making landing (4)
9 Overnight problem one found, lodging in weird mansion? (8)
10 Unashamed support given to form of Buddhism (6)
11 Decay eating into vegetable plant (6)
12 Series of events organised by female in summer in America (8)
13 Problem on the box, with end of broadcast out of sequence (4)
15 One ignites main burner in experiment with minimal load (5,5)
18 Soldiers taking extra time on march in line for dishonour (10)
20 Chemist finds volume absorbed in particular time (4)
21 Cricket score – something still seen on TV? (4,4)
24 Apply pressure within authority (6)
26 Frivolous little woman meeting head of state (6)
27 Kitchen utensils taken up as last resort (8)
28 Hooligan needing cuddle after end of punishment (4)
29 International players in fight, reportedly, at end of season (10)

DOWN

2 Let deer run around end of common (9)
3 Swimmer is one to offer tips about river (5)
4 Peel 'n' a pip is what you might get from this fruit (9)
5 Take on London football team – first half only is lively (7)
6 Puzzle about something coming to a stop (5)
7 Able to do a job, but restricted (9)
8 Palm needs region without cold (5)
14 Game going over heather and making a shrill sound (9)
16 The pub with metal cladding is an historic country building (5,4)
17 Bag journalist carried round states (9)
19 The last person you'd expect to be at a computer? (3,4)
22 Biblical character, individual elevated over church (5)
23 Sponsorship is needed to support opening of arena, say (5)
25 Fruit tree that's beginning to bend under weight (5)

4

ACROSS

1 Lively exchange of views observed on the piste (3,3,6)
9 Indicate particular fielder (5)
10 Corrupt racket on track in London (6,3)
11 Understanding exclamation Spaniards make in dream (9)
12 Hood appears to plunder home (5)
13 Miss the old, retired retainer (6)
15 Search through rubbish, in other words, to get one's own back (8)
18 Enclosure of the countryside (8)
19 Trying to avoid obstacles, go downhill fast (6)
22 Thoroughly proficient in a small, specialised area (5)
24 It's crazy to tread on explosive device (9)
26 She made a bloomer, becoming Mrs. Corcoran (9)
27 Home for animal – or for Cockney (5)
28 Blair has repeatedly destroyed ogre expertly (6,6)

DOWN

1 Assets Archy was unable to use (7)
2 As a fabric it is going to become dated (5)
3 Bad reputation – one I try to change (9)
4 Seat from which you can get dislodged noisily (6)
5 About to fish, having crossed river and cut back (8)
6 Manage a course of beef (5)
7 Court bringing point up during judicial examination (8)
8 Double up, say, in pain (6)
14 Vessel – check temperature in centre (8)
16 Lout never disposed to put himself forward (9)
17 Entertainment organiser originally setting record up (8)
18 Meat with extremely fine coating – with fine coating that's burnt (6)
20 A soldier of rank, prince follows god of war (7)
21 Main fastener (6)
23 Subject of the state (5)
25 Brief necessary to make up barrister's earnings (5)

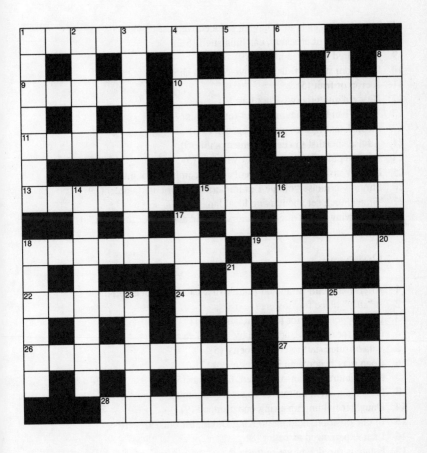

ACROSS

1 One simply celebrated, having reduced weight? (3,4)
5 Break piece of crockery, catching shelf (5,2)
9 Structured play area in park (9)
10 Run from start to finish of course, being shot (5)
11 A crop of fruit (5)
12 He's cut and otherwise not hurt (9)
13 Year's ban light, having fallen foul of this? (13)
17 Inconsistent figures given in speech (5,8)
21 Advise socialist to keep statement short (9)
24 Provide guidance as prophet, over time (5)
25 Initially visible to East, heavenly body coming back into view (5)
26 Strongly criticise volume I'm immersed in for entertainment (9)
27 Time church set about using local language (7)
28 Right-wing group of conspirators, a solid and powerful pack (3,4)

DOWN

1 After treatment, Brian and Lucy's first baby born in autumn (6)
2 A "silly" place for flowers (6,3)
3 Lack opportunity for fonder relationship (7)
4 Oscar, for example, achieved by a small cast (9)
5 Sets of rules start to cramp poetry (5)
6 Loan may become an irregular event (7)
7 Boat picture has not succeeded, for a start (5)
8 New diagram at bottom of page, for example (8)
14 Daughter holding up a ring one dropped (9)
15 In one position, holding up King David, for one (9)
16 I am experienced as better (8)
18 Estate is run down, we're told (7)
19 One knows one's past caring for this subject (7)
20 Author of futuristic yearbook (5)
22 Leave shortly before a line dance (5)
23 Foreign resident no longer a soft touch (5)

6

ACROSS

1 Alternative suggestion from bartender? (15)
9 Sort of car unsuited to a shift worker (9)
10 Scent left from seaweed on the rocks (5)
11 Fairground tout for boxer, say (6)
12 Bought what's customary (8)
13 University trial arranged in prescribed form (6)
15 Weakness for choice food (8)
18 Religious type wanting to live very nearly without deceit (8)
19 Serviceman unit discharged to become a joiner (6)
21 Set out data showing what's prohibited after usual period (8)
23 On pitch, say, a period of play in sport (6)
26 Instruments originally used in orchestra based on European style (5)
27 Outwit, getting more than a sovereign per item (9)
28 Order in the classroom going with good teaching (15)

DOWN

1 In banking, the pound appears to climb awkwardly (7)
2 Perfect voice (5)
3 Clement is consumed with rage (9)
4 Hero taking part in ecclesiastical tribunal (4)
5 Embarrassed about a lot of songs having to be used again (8)
6 Stick to administer beating (5)
7 Is it used to record minutes? Yes and no (9)
8 Trumpet vainly in sensational style (7)
14 Where traveller is charged as assassin employed by ring (9)
16 Locomotive needing very strong screw (4,5)
17 Vacation apartment is a convenience in America (4,4)
18 Page-boy may have to be pressed to work (7)
20 Unusually good R & A round hard for one who drives badly (4-3)
22 Look around a ship for such a rope (5)
24 Colour of hat shortly to appear in 2001? (5)
25 Dark horse as musical heroine (4)

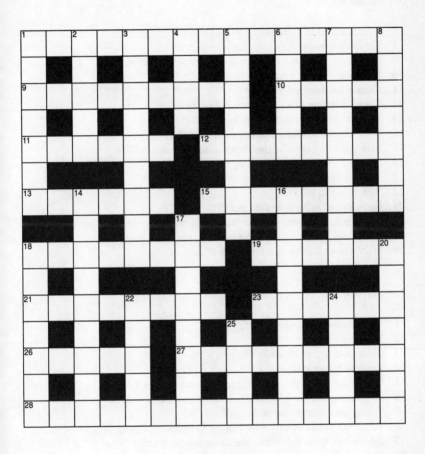

ACROSS

1 One qualified to guide holy group (5)
4 Cheeks city men (4,5)
9 Prepare to read more into record of work pending (5,4)
10 Expressing writer's emotions in the theatre (5)
11 Chance for Smollett's hero (6)
12 Model daughter in a soap given full scope (8)
14 Material possessions that may be abused (9)
16 Some terrific stories around in this genre (3-2)
17 Man following one daughter's peculiar expression (5)
19 Agnostic Liberal sadly yearning for the past (9)
21 Waiter's here with no meat or rum (8)
22 Weaver's seat (6)
25 Girl getting husband in a temper (5)
26 Retrograde plan involving the Speaker in temporary suspensions (9)
27 What's annoying about tough Cockney being tight-fisted (9)
28 Old-fashioned Democrat on Fourth of July, say (5)

DOWN

1 It takes time, proverbially (15)
2 Left port with cargo (5)
3 Switch off and go on strike (4,3)
4 Intimate blessing (4)
5 Encourage midshipman to be receptive and relax (4,2,4)
6 Muslim leaders clash violently about religious uprising (7)
7 Taking into custody for striking (9)
8 Very brief tenure of office for Christian, for example (6,2,7)
13 Ignorant as some policemen are about one point (10)
15 Fish round stern of boat, standing up (9)
18 Anaesthetic producing extra apprehension when taken orally (7)
20 Took on commercial work Edward contracted (7)
23 Sailor needing books and cards (5)
24 Bishop served with fish in accommodating vicar's home (4)

8

ACROSS

1 Flashy bird taking in a couple of unknowns (5)
4 Dance – or its third or fourth part (9)
9 Experienced the triumph of hope over experience (9)
10 Court action about husband (5)
11 News group revealing Freudian technique (4,11)
12 Annual fixture to which dancers become attached (7)
14 Tolerate food-processor (7)
16 Arresting crooner after return of Prohibition (7)
19 Tax food and drink heartlessly – and quantities of wine (7)
21 Junior officer gets place in top ten before soldier, perhaps (5,10)
23 Element in *Time*s nobody wanted brought back (5)
24 Nothing for a change in a holiday is leisure pursuit (9)
25 Old setter mangled birds (9)
26 Like some sugar? That could make one heavy (5)

DOWN

1 A lady who can be fairly trying (9)
2 Brewer's work – almost the last word in dictionaries (7)
3 Get a drink from foyer bar (5)
4 Fall silent after question I understand to be about leader of conspiracy (7)
5 Prior to cuts in book lists (7)
6 Discuss informally in excitement before a boxing match (4,5)
7 Leading lady, a star in the making (7)
8 Heard Hispanic peasant's song (5)
13 Shakespeare's omission from act, with no time for revision (9)
15 Cash in, yet possibly cause for his loss (9)
17 Chap entitled right individual to enter club (7)
18 I am in favour of an expression of disgust (7)
19 Reformation sect avoids universal change (7)
20 Element that's briefly socially acceptable (7)
21 Firmly maintained it's illegally arranged (5)
22 It spans a short distance with trouble? Quite the reverse (1-4)

ACROSS

1 Town fellow following country pursuit (10)
7 One attempting to get back a queen, a jack, and a ten (4)
9 Good oak cart needed by Highlander (8)
10 Uncomplimentary reference to Pravda's provocation (3,3)
11 Essential component of car in grand final (3,3)
12 Be masterful with maiden, perhaps, and simple in speech (8)
13 Crazy one mustn't be allowed to go off the rails (4)
15 Popular brand mother's determined to secure (4-6)
18 Boys enlist when ordered, apparently (10)
20 Negative consequence of gym being closed (4)
21 Following disorder, a leader very acceptable? (2,6)
24 Passion shown by artist for at least ten years (6)
26 Delightful nightclub with trendy interior (6)
27 Pole position, at the front (8)
28 Crazy people about to produce shock (4)
29 Decisive points in court (3-7)

DOWN

2 Woman with common sense, I am bound to be single-minded? (9)
3 It could be the future that makes one anxious (5)
4 Fish in menu is cooked especially for Pharisee (9)
5 Responsible leader of union ousted in absurd manner (7)
6 Bottle winner half disposed of before victory (5)
7 Ban fellow hanging around star (9)
8 Portuguese navigator beheaded lizard (5)
14 Working opportunity – time to get stuck in (9)
16 Cowslip, for instance, won't necessarily come out (9)
17 After a shake-up peers exit – the hallmark of meritocracy? (9)
19 Source of berries seen on country walk (7)
22 Novelist or poet getting endlessly worked up (5)
23 Heat may be needed for this uniform temperature (5)
25 Origin of pigment, one found in the drink (5)

10

ACROSS

1 Person putting the squeeze on robber secretly (6-6)
9 Does a chap have to swear to join this company? (5)
10 One may have a flutter, given inside information by royal family (9)
11 Follower of alternative medicine that's in? No way! (9)
12 Coaches drawn together to prepare athletes (5)
13 Sailor with bark, a single-masted ship (6)
15 Woollies wrinkle with continuous use (8)
18 A dark purple sort of port (8)
19 One who lets smaller soldiers join up (6)
22 Gambled and went down, being out of clubs (5)
24 It can separate ducks, for example, from their water (4-5)
26 Books are covered by this panel headed by economist (9)
27 Fish with a line, for example (5)
28 Whence reporters observe crowd largely dispersed (5,7)

DOWN

1 Radioactive discharge suddenly prominent (7)
2 Good capacity for curry (5)
3 Revision of page one is work requiring intelligence (9)
4 Low note included in money (6)
5 Welcome warmly with flower and cards (4-4)
6 Possible cause of food-poisoning, and consequently temperature (5)
7 Run out of paper ribbon in packets, say (8)
8 Leading batsman may be required to remove cap (6)
14 Those present at this reading make themselves heard (4,4)
16 Drill team breaking up monotonous routine (9)
17 Lock out of heated pool for misconduct (8)
18 French woman in state about leading man (6)
20 Game given many shots in country style (7)
21 Animal seen around East's answer (3-3)
23 Don't admit bishop into close (5)
25 Girl trapped in wire netting (5)

11

ACROSS

1 Impart knowledge to a learner without ceremony (8)
5 Card players and tribesman taking turn and turn about (6)
10 When leaders are assembled, lots of you are less patriotic (5)
11 Show pleasure about poster – it covers the window (9)
12 Nurse acquired, needing a female to look after the kids (5,4)
13 Exotic food carried by ship I launched (5)
14 Property specially designed for some films (7)
16 Bow of Oriental vessel turned to West (6)
19 Divorcée having nothing, almost, to spare (6)
21 Protective screen provided by special troops – look around (7)
23 Wit acceptable in good book (5)
25 Defender shoots and scores own goal? (9)
27 Paper worth money to socialist with varied fortunes (9)
28 A puzzle – wow! (5)
29 Helmet man, I'm sorry to say, had the wrong way round (6)
30 Author speaking like a minister (8)

DOWN

1 Person with a key for his home, perhaps (8)
2 Fielder at first being deceptive, to deceive bat (6,3)
3 Race meeting (5)
4 Pair in a race not finishing, it's so gruelling (7)
6 Self-control needed to dispose of what's left? (9)
7 Poet hasn't got right watch (5)
8 Cast some light on problem turning up in test paper (6)
9 Black magic all right for composer (6)
15 Change one's mind and pop in (4,5)
17 Dancing braves not keeping a lookout (9)
18 Swaggering about and making waves? (8)
20 Inn well known in literary circles, thanks to Shakespeare (6)
21 Strange craving to stick up for bullfighter (7)
22 Beginning to evacuate, caught in aircraft, does this (6)
24 Man said to make obeisance (5)
26 Female with weak boyfriend (5)

12

ACROSS

1 Narrator's vivid technique remarkable here (8,7)
9 Unique – one could put it no plainer (9)
10 Decision to dismiss court composer (5)
11 Smart guy to show fury (6)
12 Provided the necessary legal document without conflict (8)
13 Makin' score of ten, say? Capital (6)
15 Arrange by grade, especially at first year (8)
18 Scheme devised by bloke sounding melancholy (8)
19 Gangs amassed stores of treasure, say (6)
21 Took part, in charge of teaching (8)
23 Ancient magistrate knowing nothing new (6)
26 British forces served here initially (5)
27 Supply to French department in balance (9)
28 Pray with ministers and be converted to this? (15)

DOWN

1 Its content is a matter of debate (7)
2 Part of hair-dressing exercise (5)
3 Controlled how onions may be sold (2,1,6)
4 Day that is cut short (4)
5 Leafy ornament made initially in a range of colours (8)
6 Young swimmer constantly circling lake (5)
7 Archaeopteryx a proverbially successful feeder? (5,4)
8 Fidgeting, drunk wife interrupts (7)
14 Table football isn't one, however (5,4)
16 Judith may be found browsing in these dubious volumes (9)
17 Central Line train not going straight to destination (8)
18 A case to break Dickens' complacent businessman (7)
20 Tin-plated universal joint is light, naturally (7)
22 Gain height with maximum speed on wing, say (5)
24 Small island in greeting to Western part of large one (5)
25 Rock drill's rough sound (4)

13

ACROSS

1 Simple Simon and what he didn't have for such a pie? (5)
4 Hay scattered around damaged garden shrub (9)
9 Harmonise with one playing flexible instrument (9)
10 Settle down and start to sleep inside this (5)
11 Time of abstinence, one having left vegetable (6)
12 A chessman used in combinations, say (3-5)
14 Kid who may give guy no rest (9)
16 Sensual man was a tyrant to some extent (5)
17 Configuration of stars changes, with five obscured (5)
19 Spooner's dog, lean for so long (6-3)
21 Quartermaster? (8)
22 Warning why cue may be useless? (3-3)
25 Pass over theoretical temperature to produce explosion (5)
26 Goddess involved with love? That's her! (9)
27 Material quirky composer's about to bring in (9)
28 From the kiln he's removed something warm (5)

DOWN

1 Sporting hero – that man's style we recollected (7,8)
2 What's able to make one fit in tree? (5)
3 Around 50, it takes courage to get a sweetheart (7)
4 Flag down in storm (4)
5 Apartment set aside for board meetings (6,4)
6 Appropriately, a rugby forward's much bigger than average (7)
7 Wartime movement associated with Fascists (5,4)
8 When a bowler, for instance, will go to the ground without delay (2,3,4,2,1,3)
13 Skill shown by politician, say, getting on boat (10)
15 One gets to have faith in investment arrangement (4,5)
18 Society chaps without the skill to become more chic (7)
20 Arranged funds for undesirable person to collect (4,3)
23 The last character you'd expect to come across in Athens (5)
24 Metal band primarily strengthening garden tool (4)

14

ACROSS

1 Is this treatment not going to work? (4-4)
5 Appear to cause embarrassment (4,2)
10 Girl left by air (5)
11 Original letter (9)
12 Places for kids to race about with trains (9)
13 Piece of music in major key (5)
14 Found in a pet, child is to be scolded (5,2)
16 Press hack (6)
19 The interior of Brazil, say (6)
21 Eurasian shrub no good in African country (7)
23 Extract from collected papers (5)
25 Aims often set out in this? (9)
27 Making woman, babbling about nothing, dry up (9)
28 Seat Conservative got by a whisker (5)
29 Behind one's back, made advances to mum (6)
30 Unenterprising type employed to tidy up plant (8)

DOWN

1 Turn to narrow part, making a sort of sweater (8)
2 Maid's role is to serve rum, beer, stout … (9)
3 Drive out in open carriage, waving one goodbye (5)
4 Old-fashioned recipe used in set-piece restaurant set up (7)
6 Capital ship is star attraction (9)
7 Liquid central to bathhouse? (5)
8 Excuse fellow who's not himself? (6)
9 Turning over, skip a page here and there in book (6)
15 As dummies are, easily (5,4)
17 View that is seen during touchdown and takeoff, so to speak (9)
18 Worked a double shift? That's about right (8)
20 Mentioned saddle, referring to part of back (6)
21 Crime witness reportedly unaffected (7)
22 Very quietly slipping into user's disorderly quarters for drugs (6)
24 Form of communication between the sexes, so to speak? (1-4)
26 Coped with most of the leading characters (5)

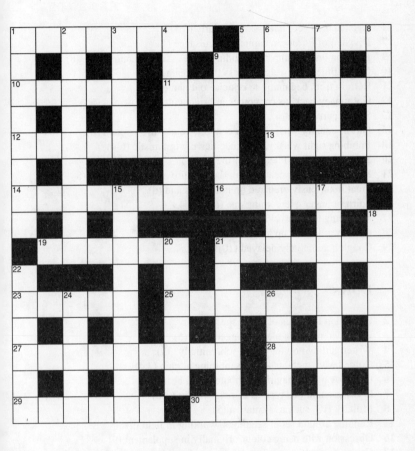

ACROSS

1 Agenda is to get *Times*, say, regularly (5,5)
7 Division of European capital is a nuisance (4)
9 Blowing one's trumpet, but hiding name – such incompetence (8)
10 Cocky little type, weighing less than a feather? (6)
11 Refrain from beginning to criticise old god (6)
12 Got money back, as car comes in bright colour (8)
13 Stroke part of eye (4)
15 Part of country where I crash convertible in narrow road (10)
18 Imbibing right whisky, remained naively optimistic (6-4)
20 No honest man is rejected for the bar (4)
21 Married love experienced, based on intuitive communication (8)
24 Treat luxuriously prepared on holiday island (6)
26 Spirit of anger overcoming one (6)
27 Not liking to return skirt I consider short (8)
28 Composer looked up to by Boers (4)
29 Cough here politely delayed (10)

DOWN

2 Protection for walls of crude shed (9)
3 Pretended madman clad in ragged garb (5)
4 Writer getting nothing out of job, initially? (9)
5 Crude heavy metal is unpleasant thing at club (3,4)
6 One took a bow, having distributed cold beer (5)
7 Confine ambitious type as clerical worker (3-6)
8 Military HQ, such as Pentagon (5)
14 Running around set of seedlings, working in field (9)
16 Obsession with using colour originally in supplement (9)
17 Create commotion, as Squeers was said regularly to do (5,4)
19 Year I had on course for language (7)
22 Powerful movement convinced government leader to join in (5)
23 Title of book one has turned up (5)
25 Son's desire to be smart (5)

ACROSS

1   One takes a hammering, sleeping rough without security (12)
9   Crime detected after lighting-up time? (5)
10 Complex structure Scotsman created initially in wild moors (9)
11 Unprepared and literally out of time (9)
12 Exclamation of distaste king let out about plant (5)
13 Remove deposits from odd parts of clock dropped in river (6)
15 No rest for the charwoman, however? (3,5)
18 Quiet area for putting outside a type of leather (8)
19 Great respect satisfies English in retirement (6)
22 Stops supplying thatching material (5)
24 A shock, partly, these being in front (9)
26 Case curtailed by underworld boss, one who's rich and powerful (9)
27 Firm top artist used as source of oil (5)
28 Agonising, learning about fashion (5-7)

DOWN

1   Each attempt to get on top is enterprising (2-5)
2   Where film stars may be, for a start (5)
3   Force rook to be taken by other piece, one that controls position (9)
4   Hunter upset Ministry staff (6)
5   At end of tether, possibly, was active in strike (8)
6   Frequent constituent of veneer – thin wood (5)
7   Specific study associated with mountainous island (8)
8   Board beginning to buy in English and European currency (6)
14 Discuss taking waters in French country houses (8)
16 Quarts, say, served in bar of old Roman building (9)
17 Salt food dried out externally (8)
18 A blow borne by the lance-corporal (6)
20 Pungent smell associated with minute American horse (7)
21 Depression in pit after mine disaster? (6)
23 Cake made by son with fruit from tree (5)
25 Island state on Atlantic supporting crown (5)

ACROSS

1   Appropriate power unit for spinning-jenny? (6,6)
8   Crackpot I mostly call "nut"? (7)
9   Decomposed matter around king's bone (7)
11 Breaking up old ring, an exclusive clique (2-5)
12 Son has to carry on packing cargo (7)
13 Head off rows of inferior animals (5)
14 Homing missile (9)
16 Stayed out too late (9)
19 In a church it is commonly dropped (5)
21 Bound to join up with, say, light infantryman (7)
23 Prepare for trouble, taking member's part (7)
24 Carried out air attacks limited defence skills repelled (7)
25 Mince pie with preserve for gourmet (7)
26 Dance directions designed to make turns easier (4-8)

DOWN

1   County girl socially accepted at the outset (7)
2   Like a certain element in tours, disorderly (7)
3   Quarters fitted like an open prison? (9)
4   Distinctive character in Macbeth ostentatiously presented (5)
5   Yellow wild birds found around marsh (7)
6   This blissful state will be the end of me! (7)
7   Undress uniform worn by some officers? (5,7)
10 Big hitter finds one pretending to protect line on boundary (12)
15 Not engaged, having no up-to-date clothes (3,2,4)
17 Major selling points of opera I'm composing (7)
18 Hide contents? Enough to make one drunk (7)
19 Find fault with a sound rule (7)
20 Part of a service where refilling may be required (7)
22 Invest – you'll find both value and revenue do (5)

18

ACROSS

1 Include in the deal the drier yield (5,2,3,5)
9 Carpet salesman needs money from abroad – about one million (9)
10 Man given a vote up front, in principle (5)
11 Mechanic with more qualifications (6)
12 Encountered a figure of speech – such as this (8)
13 Fret about a backward plant (6)
15 Jumpy, sad and moody when judgment has to be faced (8)
18 Bird dog used by the Spanish (8)
19 European field marshal (6)
21 Frees excited slave after remarkable run (8)
23 Tyrant to achieve what Lady Macbeth couldn't? (6)
26 Minister has no time for questions, curiously (5)
27 One fixes bones with hot potatoes in stew (9)
28 After dieting, one can economise (7,4,4)

DOWN

1 Over year, plant is economically efficient (7)
2 Lush climbing plant in bigger container (5)
3 Emblem of warring faction, otherwise unfamiliar (5,4)
4 Close down early – but not entirely (4)
5 How garden tool has cut into border (8)
6 Triple crown – primarily, that is annual rugby award (5)
7 Prepared for fight, said to attack vigorously (7,2)
8 Bloodsucker hit upon a victim (7)
14 Tape and string employed in harness? Good! (9)
16 Savage old racehorse upset our group (9)
17 We will argue over name used too often (4-4)
18 Stand on table contains a representative cake (7)
20 Pacific burial ceremony tool? (7)
22 Inspect bomb site briefly (5)
24 Cut irregularities off tree (5)
25 Knock out dwarf before reaching final (4)

19

ACROSS

1 Take unwanted fuel away from artist (5)
4 Reconditioned car is help getting round (9)
9 It's raised to yield pure flower (5,4)
10 Ghent changed for John, becoming desolate (5)
11 What's unheard of in island? Argument (6)
12 Line with a woollen cloth covering stiff fabric (8)
14 Enter here and beat veteran (9)
16 Musketeer takes a shot, having switched ends (5)
17 Taken out of context, rather more than usual (5)
19 Dubious books a ropy chap compiled (9)
21 Dissident's relations experience half-hearted rejection (8)
22 A couple of rival partnerships given right to reply (6)
25 Trouble afoot after bachelor escapes marriage (5)
26 Transforming GI into NCO, under another name (9)
27 Determined to hold centre stage, went off at an angle (3-6)
28 City and West End of London stocking material (5)

DOWN

1 Floor completely (4,2,3,6)
2 Make filthy hard drug (5)
3 The sort that's found in glasses (7)
4 Exclusive school near Dover (4)
5 Rich and poor are everywhere (4,3,3)
6 A drink upset over one's ceremonial garb (7)
7 Crumpled up shirt under business suit (9)
8 Undo locks and remove restraint (3,4,4,4)
13 Top person in charge of home cooking finally put this on cake (5,5)
15 Giving consent is satisfactory, but not good at first (9)
18 Lack what's heart-warming? (7)
20 Right on time with general medical unit (7)
23 Leaders in wartime have involved opposing sides in frantic activity (5)
24 Swimmer's blue with cold, coming in (4)

20

ACROSS

1 Apart from husband (4)
3 Reluctant to give fortune to husband (4)
6 Drink off better part of two pints – fine opening to festivities (5)
10 Told lie – embarrassed about its rejection (7)
11 Establish precisely why collar is untidy? (3,4)
12 Where Tulliver worked, processing raw millet (5,4)
13 Arrange about introducing one to some small groups (5)
14 Guess you'll have to eat around either four or six (6)
16 Devastated as engagement's broken by retiring miss (8)
18 Part of one's goal, to negotiate navigational hazard (8)
19 Appearance in a southern French city (6)
22 Securing article, in case as small as possible (5)
23 Angry about mixing musical styles (9)
25 Wife comes in to cook fish, for example (7)
26 Back smooth working of part of ship (7)
27 A long time to fix name for her? (5)
28 High water sailor spotted before noon (4)
29 Maltreat freshmen? It's not clear (4)

DOWN

1 Turned and drove into something, being drunk (7)
2 Man given short measure (5)
4 Soldiers condescend to listen to command (6)
5 Accommodating chap, needing to stay in other parts (8)
6 Doubt young man's title – he's a poser (8,6)
7 Hate Manitoba – moving East (9)
8 Expression of disgust about head's artfulness (7)
9 Unplayable ball may start to move about (4,4,6)
15 Abuse of instrument – not replaceable, if I should break it (9)
17 Almost support gold measure, in which one's gambling against the bank (8)
18 Music-maker provides a select arrangement (7)
20 Unusual way to replace good opening in country house (7)
21 Run into card-game from which one can bring home the bacon (6)
24 Seats I've returned, having restricted view like this (5)

ACROSS

1 Sailor on junk, a skilful feller (10)
7 Crazy flutters (4)
9 It may lessen the shock of a report (8)
10 Flower concealed by old Roman (6)
11 Archbishop Lang's world (6)
12 Unenthusiastic physician married at end of hostilities (8)
13 Outstanding feature of person in charge (4)
15 Poor me! My cart is unevenly distributed (10)
18 What can produce most morbid rants? (10)
20 Inferior work housed in rear parts of gallery (4)
21 Release item on organisation of many races (8)
24 Being careless, lose again? (6)
26 Half of sign in boarding house replaced by new flag (6)
27 Coasting at sea is uncertain (8)
28 He can turn what's originally yellow into another colour (4)
29 Arbitrarily seize public land, say, with wildlife (10)

DOWN

2 Pass in harmony, mostly, to set up rugby like the All Blacks? (9)
3 Fish in river swallowed by ray (5)
4 Whisk around with cars or simpler alternative (9)
5 How we hear of rise in value of gold? (7)
6 Southern yob upset end of book stall (5)
7 Take boat the other way to unexciting place (9)
8 River bank outside German city (5)
14 One who keeps his money in packets, perhaps (9)
16 Notes the author on the second at St. Andrews (9)
17 Single male voice showing no emotion (9)
19 Equip with excessive weaponry, making deliveries thus? (7)
22 Very poor female character brought up in US city (5)
23 Lose one's bottle in the grass (5)
25 Doctor without practice was contemplative (5)

ACROSS

1 In two senses, bear with English poet (6,6)
9 Needing lots of bread to soak (5)
10 After season abroad, some go to pieces (4,5)
11 Religious leader having a stroke has foreign nurse around (9)
12 Drunk about a couple of pints? Less (5)
13 Slip back to catch one glimpse (6)
15 Not too much greasy food for the children (5,3)
18 Trim back everything that may be material in court (8)
19 Coiffeur may use it for wave (6)
22 Star set on small Eastern state (5)
24 Minor star, exploding, falls from the sky (9)
26 Romans in a different part of their peninsula (3,6)
27 Ward off right covered by a special sort of doctor (5)
28 Interjection, for example, of soundbite (4,2,6)

DOWN

1 Reddish deer seen around country house (7)
2 Sacred picture that is accepted by school organisation (5)
3 Wicked judge accepting point in favour of bandit leader (9)
4 Happened to live on hill (6)
5 Musical fine if shortened (8)
6 After rising, frolic around a village (5)
7 Accurate, as writers to the Editor often claim to be? (8)
8 Tinker bringing in peg that's very hard (6)
14 Under pressure, striking forward and taking a dive (8)
16 Be prompt in personal appearance with instrument (4,5)
17 A cloth edge around sleeve flapping unnecessarily (8)
18 With misrepresentation, stir up pedant (6)
20 After fight between boxers, a second needed (7)
21 Give advance warning appreciation of services won't be forthcoming (3,3)
23 One's fleeced as everything in a shopping centre goes up (5)
25 To be sedentary partly makes one this (5)

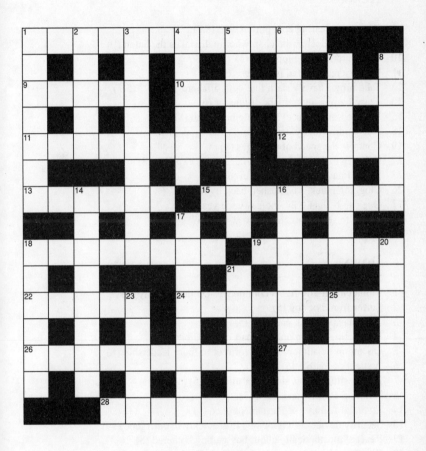

23

ACROSS

1 Dressing, wearing coat put on wall (8,7)
9 Show's conductor, the chap who finally takes the baton (9)
10 Like gardens to be lopsided (5)
11 Bird's scream as tail is twisted (6)
12 Take progressively stern line with offshore activity? (5-3)
13 Tease bigwig about mark of honour (6)
15 Rejected in favour of anything but North (8)
18 Dog's odds finally double (8)
19 Controls the speed of carriages (6)
21 Offering to god in freedom after king is expelled (8)
23 Spit – I haven't acquired a tan (6)
26 Clogging muck, say, pushed back by rod (5)
27 One can be had only one day each year (5,4)
28 Ready to settle abroad? (7,8)

DOWN

1 Monarch initially fights commoner? On the contrary (7)
2 Suffer from hot dog (5)
3 Very cheap in pink and blue (5-4)
4 Not feeling bishop upholds part of the Bible (4)
5 Quotation by author about a form of military leadership (8)
6 A street of marble (5)
7 Assess situation, as shoplifter might (4,5)
8 Whip up conflict on screen (7)
14 Essential features of Parliament once (9)
16 Security device for phone one lifts quickly in emergency (9)
17 React sympathetically about boy getting bothered (8)
18 Way French cubist becomes classic in England (2,5)
20 Cry up first novel poet produced (7)
22 In time, one coming into what's belonging to others (5)
24 Trouble with sailors below deck (5)
25 Foreign lady swindler's left short (4)

ACROSS

1 Between one plot and another, one may be misled here (2,3,6,4)
9 What Lizzie Borden did, we hear, in cask (9)
10 Foul-sounding modern composer (5)
11 Unique encounter's beginning between cricket sides (3-3)
12 Reinfect with disorder that makes one delirious (8)
13 After fall, he reportedly grasped the gravity of the situation (6)
15 Muzzle on pug modified in time (8)
18 Artist runs into a year of financial concern (8)
19 Stallion's first past the post in horse race (6)
21 Accumulations of mineral one's put back into storehouses (8)
23 So to speak, engraved without embellishment (6)
26 Reach the top with maximum possible speed, then take a breather (5)
27 Very hard, like pillars in Spain and Africa? (9)
28 Doctor's servant has anxiety on motorway at high speed (8,7)

DOWN

1 It could be why, we hear, this person is not famous (7)
2 Daughter wearing hat senorita should have on (5)
3 Military order to ignore views of both sides (4,5)
4 Cross during early part of Bank Holiday (4)
5 Ten asses giving us a new ride, possibly (8)
6 Currently batting in such a hopeless situation (2-3)
7 Rather stupid? That's not fair (1,3,5)
8 Under the influence of the judgment of Solomon? (4-3)
14 Producer of vintage Western, popular with English media (9)
16 Fix oil you reportedly processed for perfume (9)
17 Spiteful women pinching king's trousers (8)
18 A little maiden caught in bad feeling (7)
20 Bottom line's variable, in serious fashion (7)
22 Instrument from India, originally, taken up by leading player (5)
24 Succeeded to the crown, say (5)
25 Way of measuring brightness artist needed in the country (4)

ACROSS

1 Cease to associate with a kind person seen to be indiscreet (4,1,5)
7 Knowing answers, reply confidently, hesitating only initially (4)
9 Official advice given to employees (8)
10 Salesman, taking container, put back fancy lid (6)
11 Evaluation of religious knowledge, say (6)
12 Cavalier sartorially transformed after doublets have gone out (8)
13 Musicians not allowed in audition (4)
15 Too grand for meals in the open (5,5)
18 What can clear roads right away, parking in town? (10)
20 A lot may turn on this alliance (4)
21 Breakfast time? (8)
24 Like certain birds among wildfowl I shot (6)
26 Going slow, a soldier gets into trouble (6)
27 Casual underwear – note comes round on it (8)
28 Stupid person is bottom (4)
29 Old man, ripe for transfiguration, deified, for example (10)

DOWN

2 First Lady had to kick up a fuss (5,4)
3 Infatuation with a foreign title (5)
4 Bar is an important feature in Snooker Club (9)
5 Conclude drama, the work of Italian author (7)
6 Girl shared money (5)
7 Horse's alarm, encountering ring with excessively large area (9)
8 Revolutionary's succeeded in moves aimed against kings (5)
14 "Blue" applied to Conservatives – that's straightforward (9)
16 Language of Haiti open to change (9)
17 Supplier of abundant water and various rations to Marines (9)
19 Tool you declared capable of stretching most of the way (7)
22 Juxtaposition of gold and scarlet upset harmony (5)
23 Second in command coming in to lower flag (5)
25 Scientific device – one that often doesn't work, we hear (5)

ACROSS

1 Raised spirits with this description of Oxford (5)
4 Mouthpiece for launch of romantic hits? (6,3)
9 Dispassionate locum's case (9)
10 Bad atmosphere a learner associated with a musical form (5)
11 A pretentious type rejected one unnaturally small tree (6)
12 Visual aid mounted on bridge (5-3)
14 It went to one's head, being badly beaten in this (6,3)
16 Source of bulb one's repeatedly lit outside (5)
17 I had a garden tool shortened for major potato producer (5)
19 Plan way to desert a wonderful person (9)
21 An American friend, by custom, docked in Arab port (3,5)
22 Holiday one must have or break, here? (6)
25 King having trouble – knights went after it (5)
26 Evaluation of artist one's received in alarm (9)
27 With retired staff, study is gone over again (9)
28 Saucy dance girl almost repeated (6)

DOWN

1 What successful people never do furiously in play (4,4,2,5)
2 American style of cooking, taking about a month, in short (5)
3 Require another person to take the record, as a rule (7)
4 First thing needed by computer following modern style (4)
5 Quiet about his Conservative past, not on record (10)
6 Play round with defence in practice (2,5)
7 Ask to take part in baseball game, for a start (9)
8 Travelling with personal pack, going by air from Australia (8,7)
13 On which king's laid down with resignation (10)
15 What causes clot to misuse a gun (a Colt)? (9)
18 Loves the lines put in for title role (7)
20 Classic building to shake violently (3,4)
23 No use looking inside for this bird (5)
24 Navigable launch (4)

ACROSS

1 Ride up and down and shoot in retaliation (10)
7 Guarded, using two sound characters from secret police (4)
9 Struggle launched on one's own? (5,3)
10 Black tribesman's personal ornament (6)
11 Arab peasant was killed by a horse (6)
12 Family of explorers with a lot of time for coastal trade (8)
13 Fastener, with luck, going over front of staple (4)
15 Dog said to become bad and get even worse (10)
18 Valet rings with new order for tailor (10)
20 Flap requiring attention (2-2)
21 Save joints of meat for military quarters (8)
24 Great Power's political representative in Ireland (6)
26 Merchantman about to move suddenly astern (6)
27 Very eager to secure one old master, say (8)
28 Good drink, but it gives you a lot of wind (4)
29 Been bad, and resorted to here for cure? (5-5)

DOWN

2 Fish bachelor caught in Isle of Wight, say (9)
3 Quaver in excitement when husband's away (5)
4 American writer coming from Heathrow set out about noon (9)
5 Missing starter, vegetable stuffed with soft fruit (7)
6 King and Ruth turned up for barbecue food (5)
7 Criminals, we hear, had limit (9)
8 Keep silent about extremely unmerciful prison system (5)
14 Expert on language of birds (9)
16 Ring fan wearing strange article (9)
17 Fortitude of French in Alpine river (9)
19 Popular taste I had found bland (7)
22 A short hearing in the courts (5)
23 Substitute for chocolate bar company briefly put out (5)
25 School organisation importing Italian bread (5)

ACROSS

1   For so long, excessively led astray by loves (6-2)
5   To the French, about to depart, final words (6)
8   Friendly greeting from West, flamboyantly wearing bloomers (4,6)
9   Sound equipment used by men on radio for music, initially (4)
10 Belief in importance of graceful signs with appropriate words (14)
11 Shipping magnate is getting aboard a vessel first (7)
13 Popular reference works reduced charges (7)
15 In frozen sheet tossing, I feel cold? Not half! (3,4)
18 Female ne'er-do-well returned tool (7)
21 Pole's light show (6,8)
22 Rules line joining a couple of points (4)
23 Expression of gratitude to monarch about succession (6,4)
24 Raises spirit with this pronouncement? (6)
25 Last word in food, appropriately (8)

DOWN

1   Sauce produced by degrees, tucking into Mexican food (7)
2   Implore old boys to get on English aeroplane (9)
3   Simpler form of ritual, in depressed state (3,4)
4   Pieces of chicken – or eggs on the prairie (7)
5   A born composer who doesn't use bars? (9)
6   Is one retaining post for member of sect? (7)
7   Dishevelled maiden discarded outside? (7)
12 One old Greek teacher or another (9)
14 Castle foolishly and struggle thereafter – so announce resignation (4,2,3)
16 Cape spread over a painter (7)
17 Look forward to joining crew on ocean, say (7)
18 Girl of 15 delivered to a holiday area (7)
19 Page in novel Greene penned as centrepiece (7)
20 Alerts a warder this idler's back inside (7)

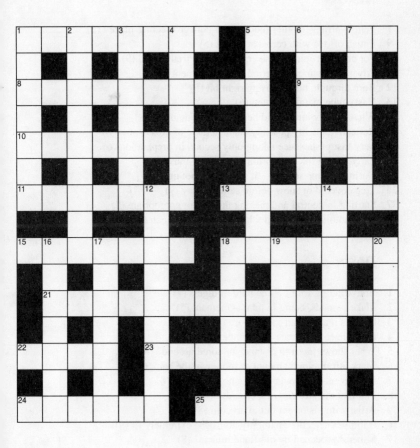

ACROSS

1 Fellow arranged other function for college meeting-place (12)
9 Finish off tea with cereal and fruit (5)
10 For cricketer joining one cricket side, a trial period (9)
11 Town flat secured in period of development (9)
12 Bore through, but not using right bit (5)
13 Nasty type mainly cheated (6)
15 What's the point of field being left unploughed? (8)
18 Reflective quality possibly characteristic of crosswords (8)
19 Very fast pasta sauce taking only second in preparation (6)
22 Party beside river performing repetitive music (5)
24 During a game scoffed – it's certainly not quick (9)
26 Tree covered in snow before summer, say (9)
27 Starting in neutral and picking third's not appropriate (5)
28 With nothing better to do, have a term of French (5,2,5)

DOWN

1 Body finding fruit cordial hard to digest (7)
2 Make amends, being in total agreement (5)
3 Offer is made finally to prepare food (9)
4 Pressure to enter race and compete again (6)
5 What shows latest in distance motored around? (8)
6 Mark left minimal amount of money in the bank (5)
7 Unconventional routes off the beaten track? (8)
8 Flat like this, let down? Certainly! (6)
14 Artist with vision set out in art.com (8)
16 It implies selection, naturally, for those extremely fit (9)
17 Mineral produced by old Rand miners? (8)
18 Cunning shown by wife getting in scrap (6)
20 Make extortionate demands for money with unconcealed weapon in US (7)
21 Source of religious law adult male's broken (6)
23 Taking part in home game, the last of a series (5)
25 Conscious of what's missing in abbreviated state (5)

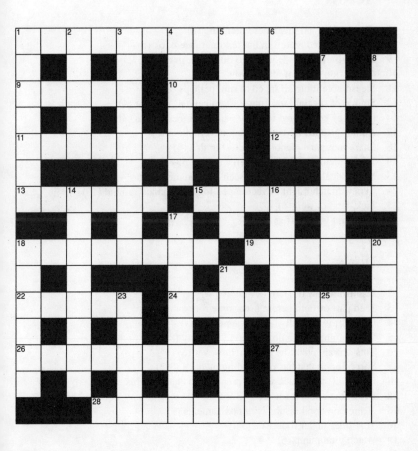

ACROSS

1 Character found in Chinese literature (8)
6 Show outdated record in limited reference book (6)
9 Improvise after trade gets into difficulty, in a way (7,3)
10 Expression of relief after power cut (4)
11 Pleasurable route arranged to rim, perhaps (8,4)
13 Source of special fare from Eastern capital, we hear (4)
14 It may be considered unlucky when their net breaks (8)
17 Author gripped by violent urge, nevertheless (8)
18 Shark may take plenty of interest in this (4)
20 Like a member of the postmen's union? (4-8)
23 Master sculptor not initially seen as supreme creator (4)
24 I knew match might be rearranged for this London ground (10)
25 Sick, i.e. not well (6)
26 Count rat going off as one? (8)

DOWN

2 Fish from bow or stern of dinghy (4)
3 Seed part of field before usual time for sowing (9)
4 Dry fruit is naturally being watered? (6)
5 What might ensure time is ten to two, say (8,7)
6 This servant could be foreign, however (8)
7 Sort of book that has outstanding pictures (3-2)
8 Unlike his wife, Jack wasn't prepared to chat like this (4,3,3)
12 Dress, then depart for drive (3-2-3-2)
15 Achieving good results with box cameras (9)
16 Tiny lines under foot (8)
19 Watch vital pump (6)
21 One of the customers in an American restaurant (5)
22 Darling pet, Zola's coquette (4)

ACROSS

1 Stupidly thinking lover is a shy person (9,6)
9 Sail North, heading off famous sailor into dock (9)
10 Cheer heard from cavalryman (5)
11 The cost of striking to plant (6)
12 One's sure to find these upsetting (8)
13 Way to beat heartless tyrant (6)
15 Hedge taking little time to establish (8)
18 It takes so long to get over Thursday, incidentally (2,3,3)
19 Get on well, mostly, having entered one new nursing home (6)
21 Shortens dog tracks (8)
23 This spring will be hot, the old man said (6)
26 Of poor quality as a painter, perhaps? (5)
27 Fed up with someone who sings country music (9)
28 Scholar, titled lady, and bishop knowing about, say, opera (6,9)

DOWN

1 Problem with battle call (7)
2 Rest of birds ruled by the first in the pecking order (5)
3 Relation arrives, welcomed by local inhabitant (9)
4 Unpleasant King, outwardly very cold (4)
5 Stuff old American had that's splendid (8)
6 No mortal wound produces this (5)
7 Idle girl used to make the food go round (4,5)
8 Pass through from North to South in characteristic setting (7)
14 Centipede, say, husband's caught in trapdoor, wriggling about (9)
16 Associate depression with extremes of lassitude and fever (9)
17 Dessert course's finally been changed (8)
18 Stuff male animals produce (7)
20 Formal greeting rudely cut short by vote for uprising (7)
22 Part of opera by Smetana that's poetically profound (5)
24 Teachers using cane (5)
25 Meat that's wasted on mongrel (4)

32

ACROSS

1 Part of hairstyle not right – stuck with it? (8)
5 Drier weather finally set in – it's handy for a gardener (6)
9 Expert discovered what's deeply significant (8)
10 Drink starts argument in Northern town (6)
12 Display of horsemanship organised in Times Square (13)
15 Fibre used in making bristles (5)
16 Worker taking pains to produce fresh milk (9)
17 Shocking, mostly "mature" production gets a nervous reaction (9)
19 Literary genre – namely, one following Kipling's verse (3-2)
20 Bill could be put up for promotion (13)
22 One doctor embraced by a stunner striking a pose (6)
23 See bull go in for slaughter as a source of protein (8)
25 Bloke, one likely to spout vociferously (6)
26 *Times* probes set-up with the French, involving several factors (8)

DOWN

1 Be critical about first of investments to lose value (10)
2 Previously given silver ring (3)
3 Brief survey of king written in unrestrained English (4-3)
4 Providing input, continued to tease union right-winger – (12)
6 – not the ideal supporter! (7)
7 Showing relevant skills, function as a human being? (11)
8 Grass supplied police with last of information (4)
11 Ring about one that is supporting a frolic, and grouse (12)
13 Rather blue, or extremely jolly? (11)
14 Ship in prime position to render aid (10)
18 Blame to be assigned about 5-0 upset is not fixed (7)
19 Determined to eat simple sweet stuff (7)
21 Enthusiast finally training a canine (4)
24 Where Tom may settle for a quick drink (3)

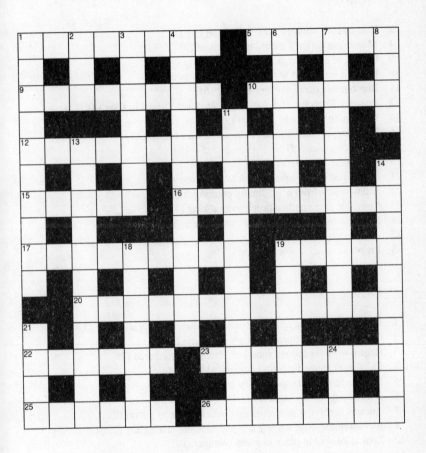

33

ACROSS

1 This castle's situated far south of the city (5)
4 Maestro in action's totally transformed (9)
9 Get rid of some fat in period at university (9)
10 Piece of bread and wine offered by holy person (5)
11 Run out to gallery to copy Turner? (6)
12 Prisoner, French collaborator, executed and thrown in river (8)
14 Damage to car lets in criminal (9)
16 They support maestri, and help opera with backing (5)
17 Drove to a plant (5)
19 Spicy snap of redhead? (6,3)
21 Period just ended square, with level outcomes (8)
22 A few words from actor finally entering stage (6)
25 Conclude fine combination aimed at king (5)
26 Heroic action going wrong in curious setback (7-2)
27 Plant or cane (9)
28 Pregnant, so some are born? (5)

DOWN

1 Unusual ideas in wedding – round the altar, unconventionally (7,8)
2 Command from censor to suppress chapter (5)
3 Return to cover second round of contest male entered (7)
4 Skirt you repeatedly found abroad (4)
5 Swan can, when trapped in dry lake (10)
6 It throws light on a right fix (3,4)
7 Ancient herbivore providing one with manure to put on (9)
8 Almost home from touring holiday, meeting emergency (2,3,4,6)
13 Lookalike shot in place of chief criminal (10)
15 Annoyed, relaxing, to be interrupted by opponents at table (9)
18 A good look round front of temple for goddess (7)
20 Reflecting how parrot is talking (7)
23 Fit to take on king in dispute (5)
24 Jazz technique taken up by Duke (4)

ACROSS

1 Repeatedly set fire to beams, manually controlled (10)
7 As company doctor, examine thoroughly (4)
9 Allowed to be taken in (8)
10 Exotic garment of little girl in family circle (6)
11 His betters support him – in literary work, that is (6)
12 New way salesman dramatically takes in inexpert female (8)
13 Prophet's body returned (4)
15 To provide an early meal, courage paid off (6-4)
18 Theatrical performance without dialogue (3-3,4)
20 South Americans in one express heading West (4)
21 Inspiring quality is found in *Daily Mail*? Not half! (8)
24 Second church exists, ultimately from this (6)
26 Star group includes a strident female (6)
27 Coward? Just the reverse – I died a Spartan leader (8)
28 Boss in establishment expected to have good breeding (4)
29 A term of French – that seems most appropriate (2,3,5)

DOWN

2 Casual worker takes remaining book on to island (3-6)
3 Noise made by chain in prison (5)
4 Refuse to go in here (6,3)
5 Old Testament character under gallery in religious show (7)
6 Sweet wine or tea pronounced passable (5)
7 How to kick drug dependence? Don't be daft! (4,3,2)
8 People as stuck-up as they are intelligent? (5)
14 Author setting a book inside ancient Asian city (9)
16 Port in extremely short supply, frequently (9)
17 How one of sixteen may be taken on board (2,7)
19 New Amsterdam today, in part, has swallowed a Dutch town (7)
22 Breaking in is the American style of robbery (5)
23 A lot of swimmers in shallow water (5)
25 Short hair this country sent up – in verse form! (5)

35

ACROSS

1 Establish colony around a port (7)
5 American marksman watched a man from the east (7)
9 Tours to Paris will take you along one such (9)
10 Used bad language, being angry about wife (5)
11 A judge having to worry constantly about illegal drug (5)
12 A handicap, being ill with tibia broken at beginning of year (9)
14 Prime Minister's distress about end of moral high ground in England (9,5)
17 No lass in a *Times* spread? Such is a tabloid speciality (14)
21 Philosopher upsetting to realist (9)
23 Go round about one Italian city (5)
24 Irish playwright, a little hot in the head? (5)
25 One of the peaks traversed in Strauss's *Alpine Symphony*? (9)
26 Hunter with the staggers? (7)
27 Encouragement given couples starting typical holiday to pack everything (5-2)

DOWN

1 Like some canine relations? (6)
2 What has insect queen on head? (7)
3 Theorize air's iamb as showing alternate rhyme scheme? (5,4)
4 Performer whose professional standing is in the balance? (11)
5 Rightful leader ousting Conservative (3)
6 Very musical attack in concert, but lacking line (5)
7 Unusual things sexy notice may contain (7)
8 Each person is always over there getting drug (8)
13 Scottish island to receive outside males for settlement (11)
15 Characteristic of the life and soul of the party? (9)
16 Former capital, but mainly destroyed with Stalin (8)
18 Not one from two in three – that's confusing (7)
19 Tough and mean – that's about right (7)
20 Completely interested in historic centre (2,4)
22 Fish has smell, beginning to go off (5)
25 Lift compartment needing a lot of attention (3)

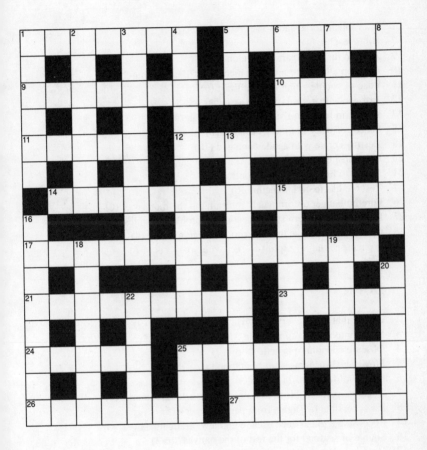

ACROSS

1 It's foolish, for a start, to aggravate hives (6-4)
7 Bill's teacher (4)
9 Want to disfigure part of London? (8)
10 Form an alliance to protect a member of Eastern church (6)
11 Race of people going downhill fast (6)
12 Arrogance to get rid of close associate (8)
13 Mountain found in Estonia, oddly enough (4)
15 Speed recovery in timely fashion (10)
18 Destroys crate with a side damaged (10)
20 Relationship between sides lacking, in legal terms (4)
21 Bound to have been out of control (8)
24 Reserve has to go into action (6)
26 Foreign banger unfortunately returning to the motorway (6)
27 Eastern and Western states meeting on problem of rules (8)
28 Cutting-edge device that can produce a good deal? (4)
29 Woman seeking to exploit worker with prospects (4-6)

DOWN

2 Clause that gives everyone a rise – or the opposite (9)
3 Mallory took part, climbing in Alpine region (5)
4 Obscure island in magnetic storm (9)
5 Flower girl speaking with hesitation (7)
6 Enemy of fox or badger (5)
7 Openers, perhaps, block initially, getting critical remarks (9)
8 It's accessible by flights from part of Greece (5)
14 Recording a piano duet, eschewing new arrangement (9)
16 Source of seafood for the rest of the natives? (6-3)
17 German prince with a country accent (9)
19 Run in to take care of one line as support for climber (7)
22 Animal found in East German state (5)
23 Moribund dingy resort (5)
25 He made noteworthy scores as English opener, in cricket (5)

ACROSS

1 Jester, one about to appear in royal house (6)
5 I'll miss gin, perhaps – almost none in diluted drink (8)
9 Fleming's agent used to keep physically fit (10)
10 Rebecca's son returned from exploit, penning article (4)
11 Oriental's pranks catching a Northern European (8)
12 Some of the crew is dominant – result of experience? (6)
13 Bond reported in from part of Asia (4)
15 Time in the capital with an ardent supporter (8)
18 What char may do, linking up with other char in a plant (5,3)
19 Get filled up, where drivers start to join motorway (4)
21 In conversation, show resentment of a wedding (6)
23 Tank designed for Siamese fighters? (8)
25 Mix red and yellow at first? I might (4)
26 Italian writer using reason concerning the environment (10)
27 What's needed to keep one's head above water? (8)
28 Law broken in other-worldly Hants town (6)

DOWN

2 Misguided aeroplane losing way in comic entertainment? (5)
3 So is butter sincerely recommended? (9)
4 Could he have taken a risk, ill-advised, about English? (6)
5 Obviously lacking instruction (4-11)
6 Infection's grown nasty inside raised edge (8)
7 Hair given very French style at first (5)
8 Disappear, having fallen out over a tape (9)
14 Asking about second person's health (3,3,3)
16 Almost call in popular opinion for face-to-face meeting? (9)
17 Rascal observed keeping friend quiet (8)
20 Strike about to become isolated (3,3)
22 Time to encapsulate Catholic's proud character in writing (5)
24 Person with 12 supporting University's custom (5)

ACROSS

1 Get the bit between your teeth? (5)
4 Shot producing bang (6,3)
9 To redecorate with mainly red coat is a blunder (9)
10 This sort of bike was blue (5)
11 Eg, as expanded by adding form of imperial tax (7,6)
14 Time not working is swell (4)
15 Eating elsewhere off one's trolley (3,2,5)
18 Lack of fairness within English constitution (10)
19 Square boundary, as follows (4)
21 Guy has to remove the mouse (4,3,6)
24 What did Grundy do midweek? Used an axe (5)
25 Mark line at note for composer (9)
27 After reform, lack power? Labour's carried on here (9)
28 Contribution to strike (5)

DOWN

1 Driver taking volunteers home? Sure (3,7)
2 Bad start (3)
3 Fight with extra energy in tight spot (6)
4 Song, primarily associated with religious service (9)
5 Conduct of hard-hearted employer (5)
6 Go conveniently through the usual channels, in such a controlling way (8)
7 Transform OK chap into a villain (7,4)
8 Spruce of considerable size (4)
12 Highest achievement of century after revolution (6,5)
13 Choose the best red tool for digging (6-4)
16 Twice call place providing basic information about work (5,4)
17 Duly pick randomly in this game of chance (5,3)
20 Get excited about diseased tree (6)
22 Protection for seed among contestants (5)
23 What change makes one become friendlier? (4)
26 Drink, non-alcoholic? You can say that again! (3)

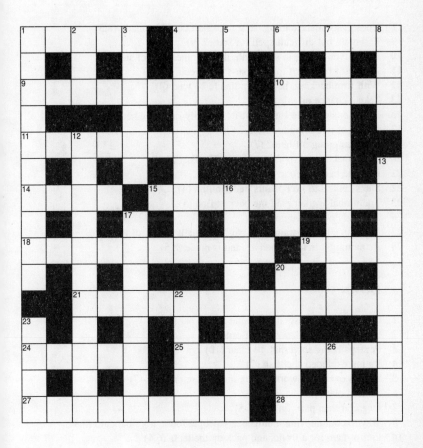

ACROSS

1 Conservationists holding on, until a start could be made (8,5)
9 Essential, but difficult spell for some? (9)
10 Flag, given hotpot to start with, then another type of stew (5)
11 Instructor restricted to later parts of his course? (5)
12 With firm backing, he's given line to be toed (4)
13 Take a chance on this (4)
15 Directions given to Lake District, initially rambling here? (7)
17 A case of not being too hasty? (7)
18 Bananas going off here? (7)
20 Some machines exported from the Far East (7)
21 Half the barrel's gone – the swine! (4)
22 She's central to sycophants' redefinition (4)
23 Traditional worker paid me back at first (5)
26 Take this when you go (5)
27 Mummy's boy restrained by nag? This calls for toast! (9)
28 Remaining a fielder when a stand is made (8,5)

DOWN

1 One's usually finished the round in this bar (10,4)
2 Implied historian's not out of order (5)
3 Perhaps being so verbal, be clear (10)
4 Rating excluded shellfish (7)
5 Dallies over hard work, where models are on view (7)
6 Section one (4)
7 Dog and man part, finally (4-5)
8 Way to contain wine indulgence – people found possible cure (5,9)
14 Pick stream for a frolic, and pack up the tents (6,4)
16 Plant informer that's not listened to at first (9)
19 Oddly heavy mask – not proper veil (7)
20 Badge worn, loudly offer support for having change of heart (7)
24 End up on motorway for seaside resort (5)
25 One with peak, on head, not a standard military issue (4)

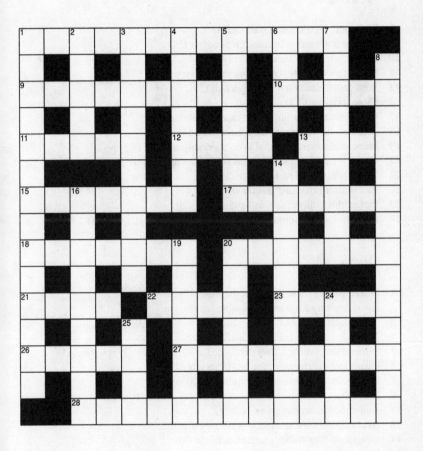

40

ACROSS

1   Malinger? Don't sound well (5,3,4)
9   Has the potential to become great power (5)
10 Shelter opening after cold start (9)
11 Most Irish characters may appear so unsystematic (3,2,4)
12 West Indies cricketers joining a cult (5)
13 Close to anger (4,2)
15 Engage in flag-waving? That takes the biscuit (8)
18 Test case in which strikers are confined (8)
19 Judge passes sentence that is considerably reduced (6)
22 Game of highest class between sides from the country (5)
24 Note distortion of reality in this? (5,4)
26 Past master broadcast this on air (9)
27 Picked this college, say, to be illustrated (5)
28 Pain produced by order leading to rows, plain and simple (6,6)

DOWN

1   Screen hiding 'ouse in unspecified way (7)
2   Noisy hostelry acquired a valuable bar (5)
3   Make hole in exhaust (2,7)
4   Feverish from the cold, perhaps, I caught (6)
5   Without originality, hasn't succeeded at first with extravagant style (8)
6   Quarrel when Henry's expelled from school (5)
7   Charles invested in simple acquisition (8)
8   Don't allow king to stay on board? Just the reverse (6)
14 Authenticate rumour about Jack (8)
16 Avoid committing oneself as a cat's-paw (9)
17 Caught on film endless time of struggle (8)
18 King Edward, for example, as lawmaker (6)
20 Duck in south hard to spot in the air (7)
21 Victor's wife given a ring (6)
23 This helps to clean up game, supported by sporting body (5)
25 Look after stock, regarding old ones unfavourably (5)

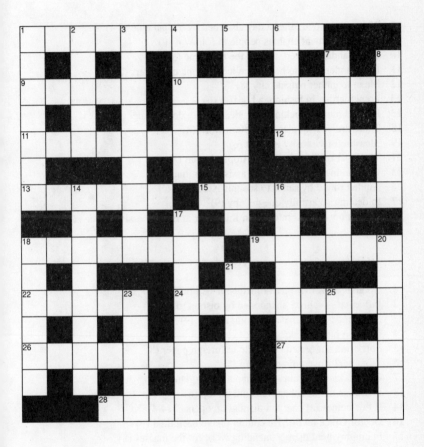

ACROSS

1 Time one retired, after a day absorbed by Trojan epic (8,4)
9 Fox's movement enables people to follow it (9)
10 Commander, elected, not for the first time (5)
11 Party understood to have expelled extreme characters (2-4)
12 Mean to gather outside city (8)
13 French artist, in fashion, a big fish (6)
15 Helen's mother backing new idea for city down under (8)
18 Tonic drunk with pleasure before work (8)
19 Measure of viscosity in fuels (6)
21 Top layer of dirt around one tropical plant (8)
23 Hare-brained plan involving assistant, initially (6)
26 Guided round by sailor to see this island (5)
27 In dealing so artfully one gets by (9)
28 Companion breaks into cheer, following horse endlessly in race (12)

DOWN

1 Good as new, first piece of triptych's stimulating (7)
2 Influence in schism abandoned by bishop (5)
3 Dish on desk covered with fruit, mostly (9)
4 Odds on batting side? (4)
5 Soft drink suggested by article in foreign paper (8)
6 Wine bar? Love going in there (5)
7 Offered kiss, bail out – one had a lethal glance! (8)
8 Fictitious plant with curious nut on top (6)
14 If this comes off can you dismiss an opener? (4-4)
16 Doctor Grace hit 50? He couldn't have been this! (9)
17 In employment there's unending work for the masses (8)
18 Flag to carry about in show (6)
20 Chief certain to retain power over me (7)
22 Small picture? It includes bouquet, not ring (5)
24 Sequence to have heart sinking, leading to mate (5)
25 Intimidate with line written for hood (4)

42

ACROSS

1 Tramp settles by bit of felled tree (8)
9 In French art work, name used for shell in heraldry (8)
10 Solicitor in south-east of France is most resolute (8)
11 Derogatory description of person's blood sample (8)
12 Character in popular success held back by a cruel emperor (8)
13 Many a seabird seen by a lake, appearing broody? (8)
14 Appear enthusiastic about single broadcast, and achieve recognition (4,4,4,3)
20 Crushed berries ultimately beneficial in special brew (8)
21 Having accepted round of duty, old nurse is laid low (8)
22 Firewood, the sort Heather used (8)
23 Neglecting son, arrange to clothe daughter in fine fabric (8)
24 Choose to join army before going in for light work (8)
25 Yellowish-brown entrance fronting one sort of restaurant (8)

DOWN

2 Name given in ancient Roman port to oft-repeated motif (8)
3 With right component, he built new vessel used by church (8)
4 Vassal runs away from European, following rest (8)
5 Fetch a person's nanny, perhaps, and be annoying (3,8,4)
6 Italian nobleman borders on arrogance, finally (8)
7 Wader becoming angry over nothing (8)
8 Old place in Malaysian island mostly having undivided rooms (4-4)
14 Mad attempt to gain trophy (8)
15 Feign illness, initially lounging idly, with box of food about (8)
16 Motivated Pickwickian attorney's introduction by journalist? (8)
17 Chemists may have fixation with this gaseous element (8)
18 Site once developed in Bernini's day (8)
19 Breathing more heavily, perhaps one embarks on scheme to crown king (8)

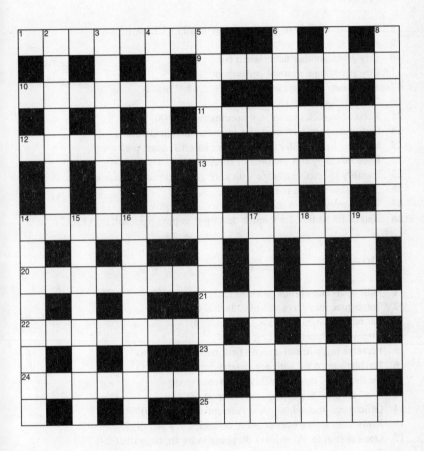

ACROSS

1 Diverting work from triumvirate on board (5,3,2,1,4)
9 Article tells about judges (9)
10 City given another name when burnt (5)
11 Boy attending a musical performance (6)
12 Make shots and runs in this – oddly, hit ball mainly to leg (8)
13 Concern for victim (6)
15 Relaxed in such classes, not needing to work (8)
18 Performance of clerical duties in government department (8)
19 Men one had initially picked out for baseball team, perhaps (6)
21 Issue raised by this member of House cannot succeed (4,4)
23 Inability to resolve trouble with university graduate returning (6)
26 Signal that may be red (5)
27 When everything in the garden gets watered, save for this? (1,5,3)
28 Half of forest lies dead, much destroyed as possible result of it (5,3,7)

DOWN

1 Pulls apart and climbs quickly? (5,2)
2 Tombstone may have this in cathedral city (5)
3 Partner no longer battles for demands (9)
4 Rugby chap, centre for Leicester (4)
5 Perverse pride in son coming first, being brilliant (8)
6 Having succeeded with ace, established advantage (5)
7 On the top of lager, possibly it's excessive (9)
8 Used coaches to get prepared for sport (7)
14 Officer you spotted, say, and deferentially salute (9)
16 Rows with author over possible obstacles in water (9)
17 Open season for Americans dropping in by air, naturally (4,4)
18 Two ways to catch a duck (7)
20 Expression of dismay as girl overturns in river (5,2)
22 Approach a vendor's position, by the way (5)
24 Lady, one originally named after kingdom she inhabited (5)
25 Miss a game of cards if old (4)

44

ACROSS

1 Capital return on project initially expected to be big, clearly (5,3,1,4)
8 Be blown backwards, to west (4)
9 Given a talent that shows from one's earliest days (5)
10 Measure of insulation applied to a classic garment (4)
11 The upper crust taking workers' side (8)
12 Caribbean association makes configuration of power (6)
13 Repeater is to gain applause, keeping time to the second (10)
16 Run ahead of what comes out of volcano in eruption (4)
17 In marsh, see river plant (4)
18 One of over a hundred pets, so sweet? (7,3)
20 Formality is big part of Murphy's make-up (6)
22 Rise to join in hymn, having found something once for collection? (8)
24 Material is short for work (4)
25 This is the way to treat drunkard (5)
26 Chap's empty complaint (4)
27 Less polluted area, but one unsuited for preserving salmon? (9,4)

DOWN

1 Period on *North and South*, say, with helpful suggestions from author (5,10)
2 Stress for poet, cold in badly-made suit (5)
3 Double sink adjusted to accommodate end of pipe in twisted state (9)
4 Facing magistrate, drunk is tense (7)
5 A losing finalist, depressed and perspiring (5)
6 Made cross, engraved perhaps, for bishop's induction (9)
7 Encourage joining club with family for unserious competition (3-3-5,4)
14 Guerrilla officer's love for musician (9)
15 Shopkeepers concerned with announcement of outfitters (9)
19 Dim ex-schoolboy's given parish (7)
21 Expedition found Roman coin among the debris (5)
23 One doctor having look round prison (5)

ACROSS

1 *Havergal Brian on Music* – book initially considered explosive (1-4)
4 Without currying, unlikely to be hot? (9)
9 Might one have EP of Kirov performing this composer? (9)
10 Frost recited verse (5)
11 Moderate showing where to draw the line? (6-2-3-4)
12 Kind person's qualities (6)
14 Wrong to take minimum outside chance? (8)
17 Town a teacher located around Crosby (8)
19 Money given after one appeal? Such could put you in the red (6)
22 What may be thrown out from an eclipse moon radius, right? (5,10)
24 A vernacular finally acquired? (5)
25 Hainault's oddly attractive growth (9)
26 Aquatic creature on river barrier that's blocking port (9)
27 Regret early part of life around university (5)

DOWN

1 A nympho suffering beginnings of illness acquiring this? (9)
2 Poet has penned nothing like the beginning of *The Raven*? (5)
3 Small chicken put right into steamer (7)
4 Agreement has succeeded in marriage (6)
5 What's behind pigeons meeting in wood? (8)
6 A token of seriousness (7)
7 Maroon perhaps that's taken off because blue part got lighter? (3-6)
8 Departed, crossing river in great fear (5)
13 Presumably nose-heavy planes need such a safety device (4,5)
15 Insect not found in France by native? (3-6)
16 Low river and lake with large uncultivated area (8)
18 Seriously block passage with rubbish in end of lock (7)
20 This hint could make for a clue? (7)
21 Symbol leading groups no longer wanted to resemble them (6)
22 State of excitement about a feature in flight (5)
23 Statesman backed by Labour henchman (5)

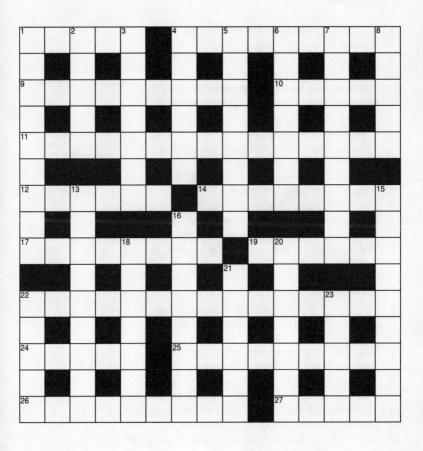

ACROSS

1   Such a view helps to reminisce nicely (6)
5   Arrived, backing posh car in, for tea (8)
9   See newly planted wood falter in this? (5-5)
10 Permission denied to construct cosy retreat (4)
11 Father, and not a scholar, expresses this view (8)
12 Originally green forest land adjoining house? (6)
13 One part of marsh reverts to desert (4)
15 The majority will get the next clue (8)
18 Splendid flower seen round edge of heath (8)
19 Enthusiast taken aback by loud, tasteless slang (4)
21 Source of short river, one near the drink (6)
23 High field put under cultivation (8)
25 Where rockets are launched from earth, zero comes last (4)
26 Someone taking part as third man in play? (10)
27 George has me starting test in branch of mathematics (8)
28 Trains, taking part in course that's rather dull (6)

DOWN

2   Are they raised to question what sounds rather silly? (5)
3   Term used by an inventor (9)
4   You don't want to put your foot in it, and frighten the postman (6)
5   Working from home, using loaf, perhaps, and a lot of effort (7,8)
6   One could have built up commitment to it (8)
7   Unspecified number wander up to tour this house (5)
8   Type of book sold that may fall off this time of year? (5-4)
14 Hybrid white rose offered as an alternative (9)
16 Head called up head of English, quite in harmony (9)
17 Leo perhaps given job, and indication how to progress (8)
20 Everyone looked for audience in concert (6)
22 Grand opportunity to smarten up (5)
24 Still beginning to shout the odds? (5)

ACROSS

1 Large amount Greek character's given knight during game (8)
5 Carry out execution, consigning chap to the drop (6)
8 On ark, I seem out of place – it's cacophonous (10)
9 Site of battle – large number wiped out in overwhelming defeat (4)
10 Treat without respect after dark – get on surprisingly (4,3,7)
11 Upset, made use of 8 (7)
13 Doorman's taken delivery (7)
15 The said lady's costume is covered in hairs (7)
18 Whose is microphone partly responsible for earth-shattering effects? (7)
21 Miss Leigh gave birth to little boy, one son on display in the blue (6,8)
22 Emulsion – not a small amount (4)
23 Identical, in spite of this (3,3,4)
24 Female bird eclipsing a male? Yes and no (6)
25 Liven up seaside resort, by the sound of it (8)

DOWN

1 Keep an eye on new technology in an uncultivated environment (7)
2 Insect, ultimately nice supper for bat (9)
3 Born and died almost loaded with money (7)
4 Fought and released king imprisoned (7)
5 Prevent girl rendering song from *The Gondoliers* (9)
6 Going off, are then given cheer (7)
7 Cut motorway out of *Archers'* territory (7)
12 Please join the army on the spot (9)
14 Yielding to pressure, clamp it on unreasonably (9)
16 Picture in one periodical Arizona's banned (7)
17 Withdraw from competition with slight injury (7)
18 Duck has nothing to eat – it may need physical boost (7)
19 I see, as you say, bird flying over calf, perhaps (7)
20 Cretin's let loose in tank (7)

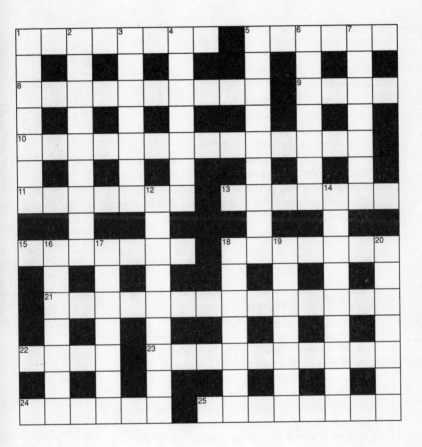

ACROSS

1 Lose track of lines to deal with one's washing? (3,2)
4 Capital of state in centre of country (9)
9 Source of oil that's the best, on paper (9)
10 From production a director selected part of Bottom (5)
11 Thoughtful *raison d'être*? (6,4,3)
14 It's inert, so none explodes (4)
15 Fungus, diseased, predictably died out (7,3)
18 Cooked soup with bottle of wine, creating a masterpiece (6,4)
19 Partners without opponents getting needled (4)
21 Incongruous use of language that might come to harm poet? (5,8)
24 University – entrance into mine needed outside examination (5)
25 I perform music with girl, as agent needed to clarify (9)
27 Light speed model – car with changes that may be cosmetic (4,5)
28 Dedication, for a Scot, could be perfunctory (5)

DOWN

1 It's bad for business when broadcast comedy is on (10)
2 Desire to get ready for Japan (3)
3 Change to plea played out in Spanish court (6)
4 State's modern business includes me on team (3,6)
5 Younger member of family bound to name-drop (5)
6 Look up year number within, to find quality of wine (8)
7 Character rendered calm by death? Hardly! (4,7)
8 Pound the poet, for example, got for a book of verses (4)
12 Gong king once used calling daughter into dinner, say (6,5)
13 Work's given to crooked person in here (4,6)
16 Aim of those with faith in comprehensive school (9)
17 Don was so impractical (8)
20 Trained, but tense in audition (6)
22 Approach shot (5)
23 Unlike ministers put in charge under Labour leaders (4)
26 Vessel with full complement of mates (3)

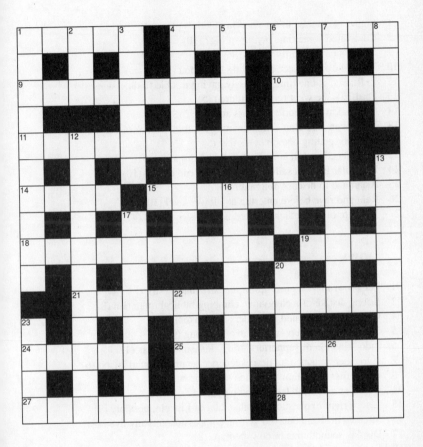

49

ACROSS

1 Sound like an ass in time-serving cleric's place (4)
3 Captivated some time *before* spring? (10)
9 Miller's name heard in the valley (4)
10 Woman carries sister, stumbling into flood (10)
12 In Russia, at one time, endlessly having trouble finding sugar (9)
13 Petrified, she wept for her children (5)
14 One making meteoric progress at Bisley? (8,4)
18 Wife overacted after drink, creating twofold setback (6,6)
21 A doctor getting one on one's feet (5)
22 Saint succeeded in embracing fellow Europeans (9)
24 Particular English sailors in outpost by end of day (10)
25 Asian had to discuss obligation (4)
26 Rant and rave before entering at a lower level (10)
27 Measure of land much reduced if cape is excluded (4)

DOWN

1 Person wrongly signed up for an extra match? (8)
2 Strong dislike of a clergyman climbing biblical mountain (8)
4 Giant mammal found in borders of Patagonia? (5)
5 Sea creature misrepresented in a lute song (9)
6 Indoctrination of supporter during cleansing process (12)
7 Agreement reached by peacekeepers operating around island (6)
8 One refusing to admit how fine stockings are? (6)
11 Qualifier given job taking photograph (12)
15 Beak's right to question an inhabitant of Lincoln, possibly (9)
16 Stressed husband delayed getting compassionately involved (8)
17 Display sound horse or cow, perhaps (8)
19 So mine might be described as particularly clingy? (6)
20 Fine wartime pilot crossing end of dam with hesitation (6)
23 Become immersed in club man just mentioned (5)

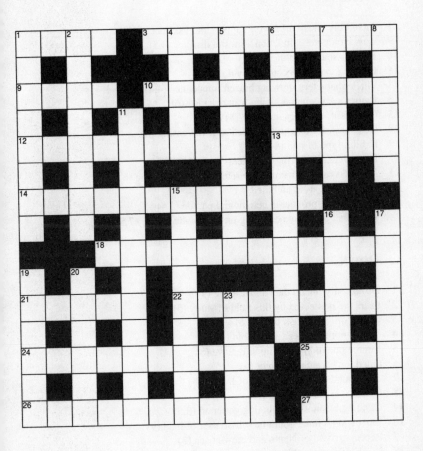

50

ACROSS

1 Incredibly cheap drinks for supporters in skirts (12)
9 New conductor's function almost a disaster (4,5)
10 Booth's seat in the theatre (5)
11 Opening carriage occupied by doctor (6)
12 Thick characters showing brazen impudence (4,4)
13 Bather's cry when noticing water rising? (6)
15 Confident, or ruddy hopeful? (8)
18 Generator, for example, needs improved casing (8)
19 Exhibit type of jam (4-2)
21 In conversation, bring up rodents and bats (8)
23 I may do casting, having one settled as English king (6)
26 Losing wife, went and died (5)
27 Month spent producing ceremonial parade (5,4)
28 Jewel that one may be putting on to provide colour (7,5)

DOWN

1 Dishonestly obtain data about horse (7)
2 Peers are possessed by this field of study (5)
3 Knock on gate to get out? (3,6)
4 Secure northern beer, when told (4)
5 Degree one didn't turn up to receive (8)
6 Oiled, or became less tight (5)
7 Tree found by river in north of Devon (8)
8 Cheat to avoid church (6)
14 Clothing business distributing garter ad (3,5)
16 Burrowing animal could be selfish user of land (9)
17 Recent arrrival of Nemo and crew at sea (8)
18 North African prickly shrub is eradicated (6)
20 Joke about girl being narrow-minded (7)
22 Precocious girl, or woman, embraced by males (5)
24 Desert holiday (5)
25 Exam taken, as the *Georgics* were long ago omitted (4)

51

ACROSS

1 Last of wreckage flung carelessly in swamp (6)
5 Turn up to mass, almost seeing dawn (8)
9 2 or 4 must have broken this china (8)
10 One day lying back on board, being inactive (6)
11 To ride, initially, on horseback, you must do this (8)
12 Died pursuing those Mafiosi? (3,3)
13 A feeling concerning a case? (8)
15 Kind of coat carried by soldiers (4)
17 Look round in the shrubbery, behind the shed (4)
19 It would have discharged fuel around Newcastle area (8)
20 Bring out a priest to face most of the town (6)
21 Swimmer turned professional, maintaining balance about it (8)
22 Pressure's needed to get one in the charts (6)
23 Insubstantial present and other things passed round (8)
24 Rice dish provoked greed – endlessly eager to eat it (8)
25 Avoid getting into deep water (6)

DOWN

2 "Bird" or "piece" perhaps heard over a pint (8)
3 Landing here after embarking on flight (8)
4 The line-up has to do – I'll be on the wing (9)
5 Rare example, possibly, where police let soccer get out of hand (10,5)
6 Where to find range of traditional culinary possibilities (7)
7 Morse puzzled over a permanent way whereby to retain memory? (8)
8 One has a traditional break at Christmas (8)
14 Having shower, with nip in the air (9)
15 When the chance occurs, remove hard symbol to identify? (8)
16 Spoil one's first award, suggesting a plant of some kind (8)
17 The *Dandy* studied without a description of colouring? (5-3)
18 Lead's pulled up dog in a bit of a tangle (4-4)
19 I'm having to talk at length about the archbishop (7)

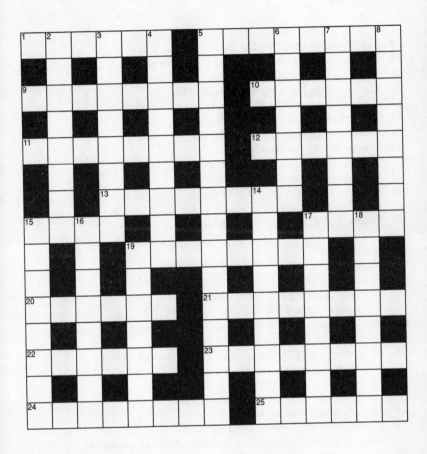

52

ACROSS

1 Nobody else could have created this work of art (4-8)
9 English county once turned to stars of variable brilliance (5)
10 Cape secured by tie at top, changed for another garment (9)
11 Asian's good name concealed – time to get angry (9)
12 Daedalus started with this sort of wing (5)
13 Writer whose work Waugh abridged (6)
15 It's bound to include a lot of numbers (8)
18 Decline European as standard-bearer (8)
19 Tent needed by Mae West, for one? (3,3)
22 Oblique request to opposites – will they never meet? (5)
24 Came across part of song in jazz style (9)
26 Look into Italian port or part of Spain (9)
27 Bother with duck sauce (5)
28 Counterpart of electric blue for girl? (8,4)

DOWN

1 Successfully putting evil monarch here (7)
2 Was Dickens upwardly mobile? (5)
3 People of a certain age look right in work at university (4,5)
4 Give another performance in theatre, then dine (6)
5 Revolutionary movement helping to trap old tyrant, finally (8)
6 Irish politicians I sent up in classic work (5)
7 Firm needing a line to Shanghai, say, in China (8)
8 Occupied with change of course in storm (6)
14 Supports British criminal activity (8)
16 Person in trial given money to eat a lot (6,3)
17 Group of soldiers, none the less, in charge of old philosopher (8)
18 Condition lifted, since company is a total failure (6)
20 Protection for cricketer cut in the field (7)
21 Fruit top-class, I found, in holiday islands (6)
23 So-called rabbit isn't from neighbouring land (5)
25 American tucked into his cooked Oriental food (5)

53

ACROSS

1 It should deflect spear, with battle raging (11)
7 Part of flock sitting here? Bird abandons it (3)
9 Shrilly complain about boat – screw loose in it? (3,6)
10 Farm animal I called Daisy (2-3)
11 Uncovered animosities – son getting over first sign of love? (7)
12 Drink a lot, or nothing, when involved in driving? (7)
13 Practice one learned after university (5)
15 Presumably for the future one follows this course (9)
17 Determined one has run out of truffle for cooking? (9)
19 Man shortly leading horse into proper place (5)
20 Outrage at gift from king Frank dropped (7)
22 Painting skilfully could be a source of serious income (3,4)
24 Old priest going on about Jews' experience in Babylon (5)
25 Before spring, bird-watching site is traditionally restricted (9)
27 Yen in principle accepted in China (3)
28 Star and entourage in circulation locally (5,6)

DOWN

1 Black music selection for dance (3)
2 Land alien nursing severe pain (5)
3 I brought in identical, extremely strange, sort of twins (7)
4 Walking stick is comparatively plain (9)
5 Greek may be offered top-flight accommodation (5)
6 In Latin, I blunder – a vain experience (3,4)
7 Man coming before me parking on blinking light (9)
8 Needed cash enclosed, breaking rule drawn up (11)
11 I see why four may struggle in domestic work (11)
14 Liking to bring up third of 17 in battle (9)
16 High Commission that's not easily satisfied (4,5)
18 Forest staff, perhaps, or other footballers (7)
19 He may return an unplayable serve at Wimbledon (4,3)
21 Chapel where bachelor has left woman (5)
23 Suddenly appear innocent, overturning verdict at last (5)
26 Stupid, given short change in America (3)

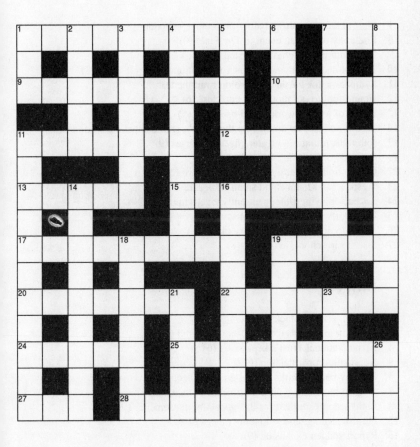

54

Across

1 Start to harvest a crop, baling fine source of fodder (8)
6 Endlessly debate an event in *The Field* (6)
9 Help with part of chassis twisted (6)
10 Type of deer about, and others you mentioned, on reflection (8)
11 Symphony, for the audience, didn't fail the test (8)
12 Hound fool to put money on outsider? (6)
13 Result of joining workers' co-operative (5)
14 To live and die, on embracing the church, shows special devotion (9)
17 Journalist initiates a greater check on horses (9)
19 One side of London is stimulating (5)
22 *Companion to Hardy* given literary award (6)
23 Trespass, and fish behind small enclosure (8)
24 Sat back playing flute, pleasantly entertaining (8)
25 One nearly gets what Manuel says – it's *most* unusual (6)
26 Artist going to bank? Not very often! (6)
27 Start 15 in school, in a year? (8)

Down

2 Refrain, given a black mark (7)
3 Dressing in sheep's clothing, one was fired (9)
4 Island National Trust's kept intact (6)
5 Nominally in partnership (6-9)
6 Flunkey perhaps lurks behind group of people (8)
7 Against including typical German or French song (7)
8 Light accompaniment for this appearing reasonable? (9)
13 Furnish seating, and help tours otherwise (9)
15 Report sudden expansion (9)
16 Second shopping facility cook shows children? (5,3)
18 Horse appears right after some training (7)
20 Check numbers about to be significant (7)
21 Two officers arresting copper? Very mysterious (6)

ACROSS

1 Old prison dispute spoken of in court (10)
6 Man's device for parts of fixture (4)
10 A goddess crossing river in entrance to underworld (7)
11 Useful feature you can make any time (7)
12 Decomposed rose stunk as a result of overheating (9)
13 Backed to excess, I would repeat (5)
14 Char wrong, say, to retire (5)
15 It would be extremely slow tackling onset of plaque (9)
17 Hotels are unlikely to become discouraged (4,5)
20 Capital place for a battle? Not entirely (5)
21 Murderer hanging about bishop's dwelling (5)
23 Dirty dance with dirty look (9)
25 Free temporary cover put round missile (7)
26 Girl I guided and served (7)
27 Complete row of squares (4)
28 Impertinently questions origin of the poet's vocation (10)

DOWN

1 Man's house said to provide moorings (5)
2 European mounts first of ads, supported by British chain (9)
3 Bob, perhaps, used to add variety thus (4,3,7)
4 Discover capital finally goes in no time (4,3)
5 Everybody upset over emperor resident in South America (7)
7 Be a prejudiced person, not using head (5)
8 Island filled with music – temperature appears to rise sharply (9)
9 To a chatterer, I'd furiously delivered a stern warning (4,3,4,3)
14 Beggar allowed to wear jumpers upside down? (9)
16 Reconditioned big limo, or old heap (9)
18 In books, one can check two examples of gold coin, once it's included (7)
19 Opera the French cut down proportionately (2,5)
22 One hiding in outhouse as a child (5)
24 Colour I had repeated (5)

56

ACROSS

1 Jerk given a lift (5)
4 King's son – the last to go and call intimidating (9)
9 Draw entailed clashing with European (9)
10 Sailor set about exercises to reduce gradually (5)
11 Dressed as Banquo, using the English dining place in Whitehall? (10,5)
12 Reveal a French maiden's request (6)
14 Wastes battered apples, for instance (8)
17 Reject girl with jaundiced look (8)
19 Fascinated – second's taken off boxing glove (6)
22 Take a walk, as Procrustes might do (7,4,4)
24 Old German stamp (5)
25 Handwriting of author, a GP, that's appalling (9)
26 Queen perhaps rang and expressed disapproval (9)
27 Fish river without charge? On the contrary (5)

DOWN

1 Restricted by petty rules, went utterly over the limit (9)
2 Moulding – not a long piece (5)
3 Respects Jack's contribution to these (7)
4 Backslapping sailor (6)
5 Expensive laundry to have to visit? (8)
6 Striking photograph scored more points (7)
7 Sufferer's bottom covered by fresh rash (9)
8 Wolf in ravine (5)
13 Miser can't have change of heart, being a villain (9)
15 She cleans mess for the steward (9)
16 Postpone work, seeing Shakespearean fairy dance (8)
18 Prepared a talk, one on a Syrian port (7)
20 Elected, long before beginning of true understanding (7)
21 Individual educated in collective (6)
22 So University fellow tucked in – as an ascetic? (5)
23 Time to find source of inspiration (5)

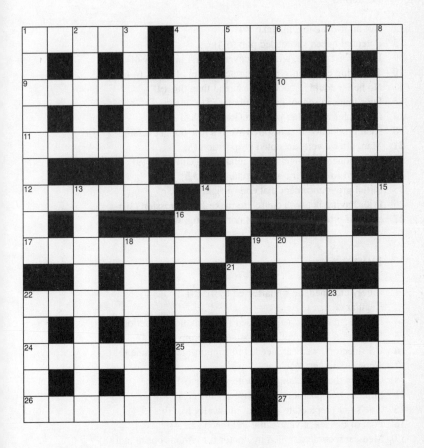

ACROSS

1 Not an irreversible mistake (4)
3 Potential queen succeeded pop (6,4)
9 Luck, for example, with bet covering first in Derby (4)
10 Terrifying experience that heightens level of shock (4-6)
12 No belief could be more widespread than this (9)
13 Poor mark in school got by scholar (5)
14 In which every other part is a Greek dish (12)
18 Rich production that inspired Weill's low-budget version? (7,5)
21 Man, after a vote, accepted proposition (5)
22 He conquered a huge area in relatively gentle way (9)
24 It's used to select the appropriate gear (5,5)
25 Initial pronouncement that ends a fight (4)
26 Prior having bet with church to make an impression (10)
27 Summit providing view – but not for long, we hear (4)

DOWN

1 Barely crowned, he's unaffected by 10 (8)
2 Regular charge (8)
4 Fine musical instrument needed for dramatic production (5)
5 Reason for bad reception of person cooking eggs (9)
6 US selectors, we hear, needed to support men in game (12)
7 Appropriate don (6)
8 Country that's certainly not without king (6)
11 Suitable compositions for house organ? (7,5)
15 One's not prepared to perform musically like this (5-4)
16 Poet of the sea, given recital in French (2,2,4)
17 Medical record compiled by doctor for famous consultant (8)
19 So woman may be dubbed authoress and artist (6)
20 Make scores of forty, for example (6)
23 Stone-carver's "Mother and Child" (5)

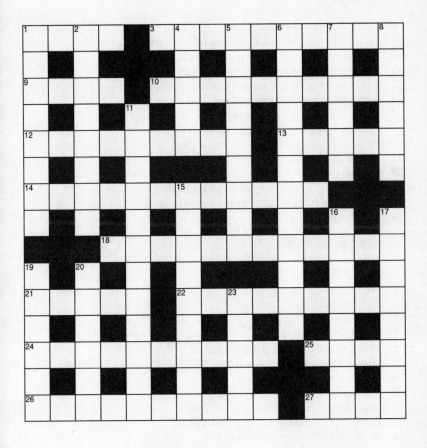

ACROSS

1 Could it be parried endlessly? (6)
4 One faithful woman – what she won't do is overwhelm (8)
10 Unpleasant person to see, with rough manner (7)
11 Does the buck stop here for consumers? (7)
12 Scoff fruit? Not off this shrub! (4,6)
13 Wind arising from sulphur in stomach (4)
15 Having a precise picture in mind? (7)
17 One who may offer health food cooker (7)
19 Up to the minute reconstruction of coal pit (7)
21 Grooves in gun barrel are irrelevant if bullet finally goes missing (7)
23 Get angry with LSO, not coming in flattering excessively (4)
24 Extra earnings available, when lookalike's called in? (6,4)
27 Cast light on Biblical city with gloomy, heartless form of rite (7)
28 Abandoned actors in the wings (4-3)
29 Spotted game being played in the pub? (8)
30 Unlike the Faerie Queen, it's no good being imaginary (6)

DOWN

1 Lying concerning copper, dishonest subordinate to head of Met (9)
2 Church of England invested in currency and made surprise killing? (7)
3 Mutual regard of pupils trained together (3,7)
5 Might one be a time a-roving? (9)
6 No persons in part of office (4)
7 What football hooligan may be guilty of in a season, say (7)
8 Artist in the modern style (5)
9 What starts mimicking you near aviary? (4)
14 Drink with Admiral in the hold (4-6)
16 Print that could be hell to copy – hard going (9)
18 Not enjoying a lift like Otis? (9)
20 Dog with beginnings of alopecia thus usually merits treatment for hair (7)
22 One father holds party for Spanish bishop (7)
23 Like a completed crossword, half-heartedly sent in to newspaper (5)
25 Accompany at a distance (4)
26 Mind one leaves some breakfast cereal (4)

59

ACROSS

1 Quietly grumble, rejecting drink twice (6)
5 Servant, along with mother, took cover outside (8)
9 Biscuit fellow turned over after funny remark (8)
10 These bones are more rigid, so it's said (6)
11 Bliss, possibly, for one who scores runs (8)
12 Miss living in Barcelona? (8)
13 Agitated former partner summoned to appear in court (7)
16 A shepherd's work takes some beating – having change of heart? (7)
20 Have regard for feelings of judge (8)
22 Improper to appear in university, only just missing first (8)
23 Errant type once given place on board? (6)
24 Short break for people of various classes (4-4)
25 Severe operatic prince interrupting wake finally ejected (8)
26 After year on river, went off to place indicated (6)

DOWN

2 Pure in make-up, but not fully developed (6)
3 Dandy that appears dishy, from Italy? (8)
4 Contact bloke on eastern border of enclosure (8)
5 Sort of gear a learner replaces on leaving Greek mountain (7)
6 Arrange to meet girl to tour Lima – it should bear fruit (4-4)
7 Party for some who may have gone downhill fast (5-3)
8 Late Australian sheep-shearer's lookalike (4,6)
12 Dupe *Observer* over this material? (10)
14 Two-timing double missing trip on ferry? (8)
15 Trio on river, including quiet farm-worker (8)
17 Female collaborator seen round university at regular intervals (8)
18 Resort of bishop with progressive views (8)
19 In South Carolina they designed sails, initially, for cutters (7)
21 Appear to be upset, say, about this compiler (6)

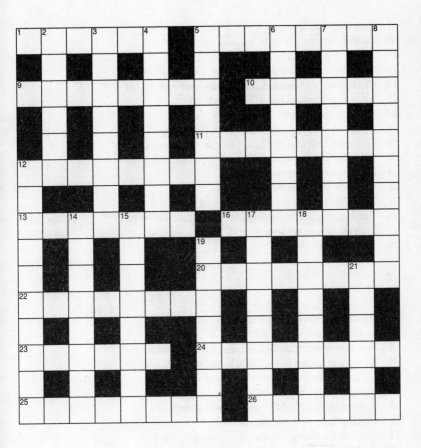

60

ACROSS

1 Turn round here to give a lift? Blow the girl! (8)
5 Point debatable – hard to iron out (6)
10 Have great success by forty, on radio? (5)
11 Sing-song and a few drinks, around university? (9)
12 Change one's expression, rant wildly, and criticise (9)
13 Adam's follower is big in New York (5)
14 Overindulge in backing horse, evoking pithy comment? (7)
16 Secure clothes in fashion, however, at first (6)
19 Favourite type of wood inlaid for part of fittings (6)
21 OK, what are you up to? (7)
23 Being in error, perhaps? (5)
25 Sport involved speed – flat out (9)
27 High-flier given a bit of support about following article (9)
28 One needs government backing – the old, old story (5)
29 Rig clear round for little Tom (6)
30 Had eager spin bowler? (8)

DOWN

1 One may be gripped by Nelson's achievement (8)
2 Rotten centre in a fruit (9)
3 Fine examples of ormolu, lustrous to some extent (5)
4 Bow when hauled in by NCO, in attempt at humour? (7)
6 Unlikely character perhaps had some substance, outwardly (3,6)
7 Alternatively, cut the deck (5)
8 Old yen died, stifled by female, once a lively one (6)
9 Excellent! B– marvellous! (6)
15 High bridge among outstanding features? (5,4)
17 Studiously avoid capsizing vehicles in French river (9)
18 One's output is all very fine, but essentially unreadable (8)
20 Put up with crew seeing Tracy in the papers? (6)
21 Outrageous cost to secure this breed (7)
22 Became less quiet, having a row (6)
24 Paid to get books in for composition (5)
26 One involved in jazz society (5)

ACROSS

1 Make critical comment, with publicity, on a game (10)
7 Robin Hood, for one, was more cunning than this (4)
9 German – like Berlin, for example (8)
10 Unhealthy state? Certainly (3,3)
11 Odd turn of phrase for form-master? (6)
12 Food store? True, in a manner of speaking (8)
13 Recommendation to strike (4)
15 Popular protest about despicable person in charge (10)
18 With code reversed, letters misdirected to NY address (4,6)
20 I'd heard, but not seen? On the contrary (4)
21 A vessel out on its own? That's a joke (3-5)
24 Fruit couples initially collected from town market together (6)
26 WW1 leader misidentified in terms of nationality? (6)
27 Extremely fine transport organisation led by Henry (8)
28 For sound, sensible reasons (4)
29 Humour head before case in which evidence is provided (7,3)

DOWN

2 Sort of love that can never last for long? (9)
3 Finally clear away part of litter after short time (3,2)
4 Cast doubt on record run? Correct (9)
5 It could make me a lord (7)
6 Test pilot (5)
7 Make light of everything I have taken up and consumed (9)
8 Support for one behind university's position (5)
14 Beat up with chain, of course, by the seaside (4,5)
16 Have little spare time to make fettucini? (3,2,4)
17 Written in Latin, at full length – No. 16, possibly? (2,7)
19 Within which, we hear, corn's heated (7)
22 Statesman, former of a novel partnership (5)
23 Expertise in speaking? Certainly not! (5)
25 Chap as good as misses, it's said (5)

ACROSS

1 Before opening of dump litter is turned away (7)
5 A bit of an ass, this Biblical slayer (7)
9 Question brief announcement of train (5)
10 Girl short with chap belonging to rugger club (9)
11 Disguise one's writing in enclosed poem (6)
12 Priest working, for example, to back reputation (8)
14 Senior citizen job centre left to fade away (5)
15 Larks making deceptive turns aloft (4,5)
18 Designed ample set including one type of photography (4-5)
20 Camp, say, where you can park for a drink (5)
22 Where the traveller may get out in France? (5-3)
24 Stripe could be assessment of military status (6)
26 Added notes, changing to andante (9)
27 Sending-off from English team the Spanish overturned (5)
28 I speak slowly at first, looking into gift, perhaps, when retiring (7)
29 Girl informed about source of vitamin C (7)

DOWN

1 A cheese needed for game starting off outside (9)
2 Removed coat to be taken to the cleaners (7)
3 Veronica runs away from drunken party to be at home? (9)
4 Small amounts of flounders, for example (4)
5 Makeshift panel tampered with (4-6)
6 Shawls in box wife picked up (5)
7 Nothing to be binding in this judgement (7)
8 His draws always turn out to be winners (5)
13 Inform on Jack as a thief (10)
16 Cheerful quality appropriate to a Marine? (9)
17 Dump old crate here (5,4)
19 Factor in many a battle (7)
21 Knight wearing glittering decoration (7)
22 Noisy exercise in wooded area (5)
23 Have some shown a talent from birth? (5)
25 Make new effort to go up river (4)

63

ACROSS

1 Crustaceans – almost the very same river contained (6)
5 Excellent score after mishit at golf (3-5)
9 He has agreed to direct steering of farm vehicle (10)
10 Make tea in hospital (4)
11 Representative from Georgia participating in strike (8)
12 Flower trouble had returned (6)
13 Ammunition is exhausted (4)
15 Non-English herb given name relating to Church of England (8)
18 Fruit clearly contains an insect (8)
19 Row producing audible evidence of grief (4)
21 Part of answer verified as "deviation" (6)
23 Policeman reversed into deer, showing aggression when driving (4,4)
25 Prevent large amount of money being withdrawn (4)
26 Cruelly-used girl and I in more trouble (4,6)
27 Benjamin Roosevelt (8)
28 Grandiloquent nonsense – and in German too! (6)

DOWN

2 Tightly shut (5)
3 Home at ten, willy-nilly? That's outdated (4-5)
4 At home taking a holiday, somehow (2,1,3)
5 Active Northern boatmen, naturally at ease when working (2,3,6,4)
6 Chart turned up containing a grid that's wrong, for example (8)
7 *The Sound of Music* lacking a certain energy? (5)
8 Players I confine to quarters and rebuke severely (9)
14 Cistern is intended to stand up (4,5)
16 Forbid indirect manoeuvring before time (9)
17 Middle Eastern money supporting China appears very relevant (8)
20 Your holding novel up causes complaint (6)
22 Grow older in state prison (5)
24 Eco-friendly marijuana (5)

ACROSS

1 Possibly the result of shrinking page inserted (4)
3 Bird flying around there was a rook (10)
9 Interpreted, for example, cardinal's pronouncement (4)
10 Religious experience necessary to achieve a goal (10)
12 Removed from broadcast, being out of tune? (3,3,3)
13 Form of insect – imagines more than one (5)
14 As guard's intended, releases from prison in Australian town (5,7)
18 Person seeking reward has watch put on Christian's vessel (6-6)
21 Fuss about one son for so long (5)
22 Is one about to be in for the role of a pigeon? (9)
24 Female names deadly plant (10)
25 Tables, perhaps, turned at short notice (4)
26 Poet of considerable standing? (10)
27 Young group settled here, some without a house (4)

DOWN

1 Soldier dealing with a body (8)
2 Don't cheat with two types of entertainment (4,4)
4 Bent piece of metal attached to a pipe (5)
5 Notice model in extremely difficult circumstances (9)
6 Free food for the unemployed? No, no! (7,5)
7 Expect rising on North Pacific island (6)
8 Very large amount if it's for royalty children's author reported (6)
11 Principal senior officer (5,2,5)
15 Source of drink creating depression in the land (9)
16 Law that annoyed Americans in South Florida city court (5,3)
17 Disorder at harbour after you reportedly left port (8)
19 Lifting equipment one left out for fish (6)
20 What Holmes sometimes got out of case (6)
23 See bat circle fruit-tree (5)

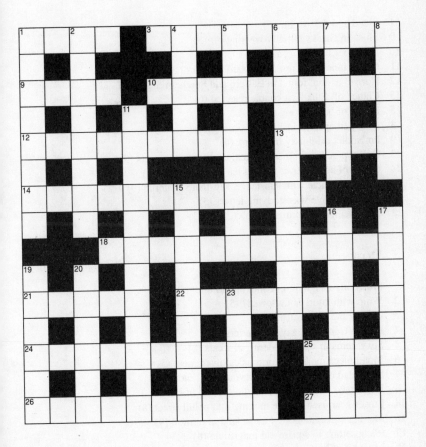

ACROSS

1 Stand and deliver (4,3,5)
9 Flush in cheeks initially wearing off (5)
10 No-hoper left Brent, say (4,5)
11 Out to lunch, where the standard is high (2,3,4)
12 Horned animal found in Eastern and Southern States (5)
13 Choice of drink first couple rejected (6)
15 Result of bad hearing (8)
18 Bob, perhaps, means to save time (5,3)
19 Pot addict originally into drink (6)
22 Out of practice, in messy situation when game starts (5)
24 Result of adding one, six and ten should be odd (9)
26 Standard article with substance, say, that's material (9)
27 Nymph in love was studying letters (5)
28 Two members making a bomb (2,3,3,1,3)

DOWN

1 Protecting daughter, opening up old umbrella (7)
2 Whip with knots not allowed? (5)
3 Got up and dressed (6,3)
4 Drink? Good peg, say, for starters (6)
5 Sexy items in stock modern girl wears (8)
6 Mouthpiece, possibly, for musical instrument (5)
7 Spot head of ounce, feline, devoured by another (8)
8 Keen, take trouble understanding set-up of Net (6)
14 Lower gear used by one moving into uphill street (8)
16 Moving consignment by air to land in turmoil (9)
17 It's upsetting to square old magistrate (8)
18 Little bit of butter and jam (6)
20 Looking guilty, suspend a setter? (7)
21 A cutting's sprung up in certain beds (6)
23 Royal attendants with no love for a Republic (5)
25 Model left after some thought (5)

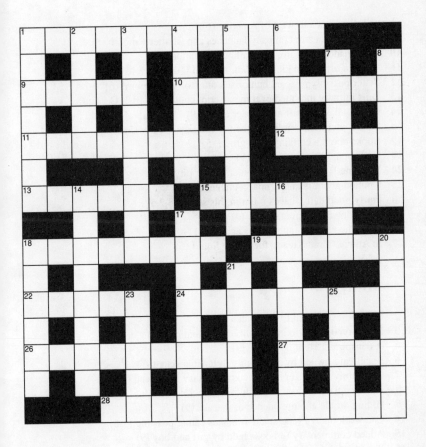

ACROSS

1 Jellyfish in sea to west of America (6)
5 Run-down theatre company launches appeal after a month (8)
10 Gibe made by Figaro, say, without hesitation (4)
11 Yesman offered to kick alcohol, it's said (10)
12 Setter possibly rejected humorist's clue for wading bird (6)
13 Dips initially into medieval manuscript containing Irish Gaelic (8)
14 He may have a craft and master at sea (9)
18 Italian who made violins in the morning, very early (5)
19 Books about a certain music group (5)
20 Understanding an assembly (9)
24 Way one is taken in and so on, arousing pity (8)
25 Opinion about island is unacceptable (6)
26 Fairly good daily leaves room in this state? (3,2,5)
27 Bring down fastening device (4)
28 One who recovers and judges again? (8)
29 In Athens, almost ready for a little liquid (6)

DOWN

2 Girl endlessly keen to captivate (7)
3 Not curved, like violin parts needing attention? (7)
4 A conspirator right up a tree! (7)
6 Small café owned by yours truly in terrible state (9)
7 Constantly repeat ceremony, taking ecstasy and speed (9)
8 Asian captain is shaken, about to be replaced by king (9)
9 Hiding article about evidence of disease (9)
14 Can work upset Frenchman? It makes eating possible (3-6)
15 Added commentary to books held by girl and boy (9)
16 Boned steak from croft, oddly served in dish (9)
17 Size of attractive bar, say, due to be developed (9)
21 Flattering husband closely observed on entering (7)
22 Rubbish a French attorney noticed round building (7)
23 Old stone implement misplaced in hotel (7)

ACROSS

1 Millions impatient to meet giant (5)
4 Church musicians, say, who agitated for reform (9)
9 Drove away from fell that holds charm (9)
10 Uninspired writer holding first of essays to get mark above a C (5)
11 Charitable helper offers possessions – a ton carried by Robin's girl (4,9)
14 In Oxford, something beneath an upper second in Spanish – come on! (4)
15 His criminal activities set tongues going (10)
18 Prepared a table, but not competent to take cash (2,3,5)
19 Terrifying man wanting bloodshed – love to go to the front (4)
21 Ride continually up and down and wave to ship (6-7)
24 The animal to shoot at first (5)
25 Began dietitian's new formula (9)
27 Off TV I do finally store copy here (9)
28 Piece of wood fitted with blade at end? (5)

DOWN

1 Very keen old commander's transport to island (10)
2 In dropping pressure, struggle to breathe air (3)
3 Unctuous, when former foreign minister's about (6)
4 Flower girl appearing in pantomime (9)
5 Cut top off less leafy tree (5)
6 Artist captured a horse, typical Gauguin subject (8)
7 Back great deal, being aware of future potential? (6,5)
8 Writer heard to be full of bitter irony (4)
12 Made impossible to see – do again in bold letters (11)
13 Bright as one whose views are of unrestricted general import (4,6)
16 Secreting directly into blood, new drug upset timeless principle (9)
17 Comfortable fit – daughter can get in as well (4-2-2)
20 Bone from old Persian king whose top half is dug up (6)
22 Queen's lost wager with husband – it's a girl! (5)
23 Shady dealer turned up kings and queens? (4)
26 Obligation to secure equal outcome (3)

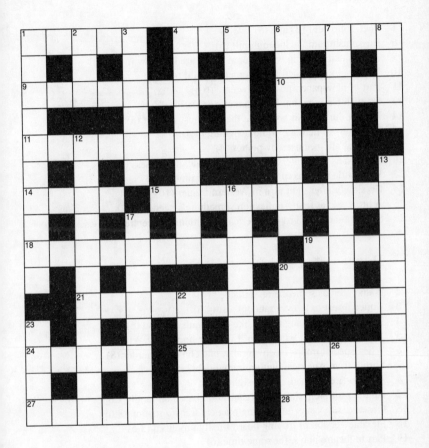

ACROSS

1   Poet, follower of Dante (8)
6   Buy mushroom, included in bill (6)
9   Pleasant situation in which some wines are laid down? (3,2,5)
10 Washington provided for a homeless child (4)
11 Part of newspaper, possibly recent? (6,6)
13 Scottish baron taking Englishman's castle (4)
14 Mother during visit providing the strongest support (8)
17 Not prone to lie thus, withdraw claim (4,4)
18 Political alliance used by plotter (4)
20 As soon as king enters court, project state of alertness (7,5)
23 What little remains of naval vessel over time (4)
24 Go slowly after tight turn in Western fighter (10)
25 A little pale at first – indication something's needed (4,2)
26 Star embraced by girl in American entertainment centre (3,5)

DOWN

2   Pound seen as someone remarkable? (4)
3   Notice threat to king in random test (4,5)
4   Italian city producing things like doughnuts? Not so (6)
5   Not the part of car where you'll find the horn, however (10,5)
6   When special troops lapse morally, one commits murder (8)
7   Shrink from American with minimal debt? (5)
8   A camp-fire I ruined, at first sight (5,5)
12 Highly profitable stateside organisation based on family values (4,6)
15 Observe, say, coins undergoing magical transformation (3,6)
16 Flexible version of ironing board finally produced (3-5)
19 Part in theatre plays, for some time (6)
21 The length of a radius, approximately (5)
22 Cheese removed from café table (4)

69

ACROSS

1 Character pictured after tuning radio, angry (6,4)
7 Spice Girl embracing Conservative leader (4)
9 Old Italian, that is to say, steeped in violent nature (8)
10 Right to make move overseas – going by ship? (6)
11 Oriental's holy book containing some point (6)
12 Hit man being an idiot, when wrong (8)
13 Island surfer's language? (4)
15 Cause a delay, we hear, wanting a little extra (10)
18 View on life and love held by boy and girl (10)
20 Fare printed in timetable at station (4)
21 Possible setback with deliveries coming to end (4,4)
24 Doctor could be imprisoned for caper (6)
26 Composer taking chance with new intro? (6)
27 Old age that is possibly perfect for me? (3,5)
28 Bury, say, is a town near Manchester (4)
29 Instrument used to jam TV (7-3)

DOWN

2 Treating stoop, he may take a short time (9)
3 Guarantee son's lost temper (5)
4 Casual references to people in jail? (9)
5 Loot perhaps includes smuggled wine (7)
6 End of play worries dramatist (5)
7 Low light conceals new load of rubbish (9)
8 One barking first couple of orders previously caught soldier (5)
14 Doctor we call on a lot, perhaps (9)
16 Considers, say, some poultry for printers' picnic? (9)
17 Awkward situation – is one in a stew? (3,6)
19 As usual, beautiful woman cut short upstart (7)
22 Green seen from field on both sides of fairway (5)
23 In classic situation, man (American) contracted disease (5)
25 Fly, for instance, lower, needing to climb (5)

ACROSS

1 Is one in bed? Part of ear's given recurrent trouble (7)
5 Opportunity to bug first drinking place (7)
9 Garment almost too close-fitting (5)
10 It takes the lid off money available to the queen (3-6)
11 One who makes an indelible impression on people (9)
12 Radioactive gas caused fuss in the Navy (5)
13 Concession about a Lad's introduction in Shropshire once (5)
15 Cushion the effects of long sittings (9)
18 Maidens perhaps shut up, having been extravagant (9)
19 Attitudes taken by half-hearted sheriffs' men (5)
21 Money king's left a composer (5)
23 Money row in food queue (9)
25 Constitutional change for Nigerian democratic leader (9)
26 Nymph errant, Diana (5)
27 Implement change, to a greater extent (7)
28 More modest legal objection – less resistance? (7)

DOWN

1 Building is to let – that's an understatement (7)
2 Trifle with beautiful woman toting a gun (9)
3 Races in for card-game or numbers game (5)
4 Assign property (9)
5 A conviction, whichever way one looks at it (5)
6 Device preventing leaves from scattering (5-4)
7 Admitted knight coming in was in debt (5)
8 One interrupting Silas is a seaman (7)
14 Carrier available for a small charge (9)
16 Having a high temperature preceded rash (3-6)
17 One who may declare in match providing that's right (9)
18 Away team is ahead of the ball (7)
20 Ann Page's suitor is inadequate (7)
22 Financial backer's viewpoint finally raised (5)
23 Imbibing extravagantly, in essence? (5)
24 Material dug up (5)

ACROSS

1 Active agent protecting king (4)
3 Cunning old people, including one mathematician (10)
9 Little cash available for old Indian woman (4)
10 One who should be avuncular could be a cruel gent (5-5)
12 A politician with nothing on, escorted round and made to look silly (9)
13 Volunteers to cut down military language (5)
14 You and I left quietly with unusual item, a type of dish (5,7)
18 Something intolerable caused problem for milk monitor? (3,4,5)
21 Protein supplied energy, with nothing wasted (5)
22 Someone standing on ceremony who experiences changes? (9)
24 Old-fashioned gentleness from fellow and girl playing duet (10)
25 Crazy alternative to the auto? (4)
26 Division in the church barring some from the altar? (4,6)
27 Beat characters in game after a turnround (4)

DOWN

1 Reluctantly accepts adequate criterion for summer being here? (8)
2 Respond in fear, as less athletes do these days? (3,1,4)
4 Raced off again, having bodged most of errand (5)
5 Ceremonial band introducing ambassador before speech (9)
6 Man dies, out in storm where one's exposed to the cold (12)
7 Walked up, embracing maiden – to elope? (6)
8 She has to have an impact, showing external oomph (6)
11 Preside at award-giving ceremony and offer hospitality (2,3,7)
15 Everyone needs one gun, or this creature might snap at you! (9)
16 One getting a series of thumps appears odd, swallowing drink (4,4)
17 Actress Gloria has good final performance (4,4)
19 It may knock a lot down (6)
20 Strong liquor isn't drunk before match (6)
23 Become confused as tot beginning to learn English (5)

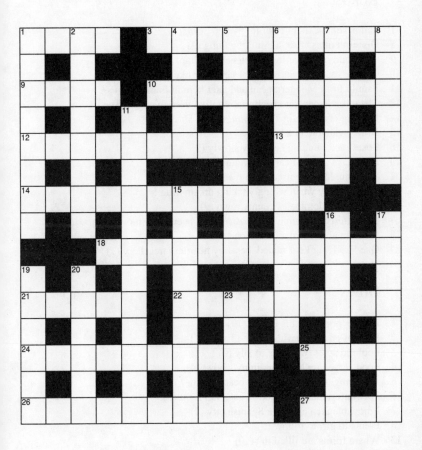

72

ACROSS

1 Sailor volunteers in error to give up drink (7)
5 Discern tailless fish, a glittering thing (7)
9 A method of delivering sweetener for Chinese criminals (5)
10 Callow youth speaks about western star like J Wayne? (5,4)
11 Family from Mediterranean and later here in France? (6)
12 Metal implements no backward conflict used in anger (8)
14 Leading character in *The Taming of the Shrew* (5)
15 Drink available in a bar? (9)
18 Loses race, running heat very slowly (9)
20 Fish that's netted I carry in triumph (5)
22 What might make user tilt to read it? (8)
24 I feel dismay when wrongly taking dream drug (4,2)
26 Rebuilding dominates county town (9)
27 Characteristic beginning to passage has been written out (5)
28 Problem about bird's breastbone (7)
29 One like King Lear ranted, beset by heartless treachery (7)

DOWN

1 Like George, like his Pianola (9)
2 Perhaps envy girl with no date fixed up (4,3)
3 Fool old spies over note to ally (9)
4 Food served up hot to mummy's boy? (4)
5 What might be generated by beam-engine? (5,5)
6 Poet unfortunately unread? That's not right (5)
7 Enjoyable area around a Spanish city (7)
8 Points to girl to follow (5)
13 Where forms are filled in? (10)
16 Band rose to become involved with chart (9)
17 Seriously immature, going outside to brood (9)
19 Certain about little girl being last (7)
21 Brilliant line omitted by poet (7)
22 Island home to saint and prophet? (5)
23 Brand originator is still burning about maddening complaint (5)
25 Run and hide (4)

73

ACROSS

1 State school in a rut, after shake-up, gets top grade (5,8)
8 Unruly crowd captures a kingdom of old (4)
9 US student getting a third in music? (5)
10 Bumpkin would appear extremely dense in test (4)
11 Substitutes suffer wrongdoing (6,2)
12 Income squandered, alas, by railway (6)
13 Balls, of course, put back after game (10)
16 Fool, namely, with nothing to lose (4)
17 Girl seems mean – oddly deficient (4)
18 Record *Today* and turn off? (10)
20 Extremely ratty, this? Possibly (6)
22 Tract written by international group is out of the ordinary (8)
24 Fellow curled lip, confiscating drug (4)
25 Hack, and what it could make you when speaking? (5)
26 Cadence in one of *The Four Seasons* (4)
27 Homework outstanding before term – one's engrossed in it (13)

DOWN

1 Attach movie camera to part of body, and express oneself freely (5,4,3,3)
2 Headdress not crown for the Pope (5)
3 Conned about politician's non-alcoholic drink in London district (9)
4 Incidental music producer, foreign one, taking part in performance (7)
5 Minor risks with potted plant (5)
6 This could be the solution to a rhinal problem (9)
7 Binding chief, captured by a tribe as intended (9,2,4)
14 Dance and music test's second part follows question and answer exercise (9)
15 They're flaming remarkable things (9)
19 Contemptible people in jets (7)
21 Brute gives expression of derision, then ducks (5)
23 Legal expert's general habit (5)

74

ACROSS

1 Judges say what's to be thrown at an offender? (4)
3 Leader of council's brought in place for rubbish at little cost (2,3,5)
9 Daughter banished from landowner's den (4)
10 Flier backing the German leading seaman (3,7)
12 Bank on including unfashionable and fashionable in the usual way (9)
13 Speech cut at both ends to maintain proportion (5)
14 Specially-designed prop deteriorates with use, but holds one still, ultimately (7,5)
18 Freudian concept is corny, say, garbling personal quirk (12)
21 Female encompassing the French ideal of beauty? (5)
22 Get better of editor with paper? Wishful thinking! (4-5)
24 Padre? (10)
25 Gentle Liberal brought in with obscure backing (4)
26 One seeing ball stopped by upraised hands? (10)
27 Asking to strip off, to display this? (4)

DOWN

1 One's hung in the Tower to help give a warning to people (4-4)
2 Article commenting on end of note? (8)
4 Relative in Greece injured in uprising (5)
5 Long-lasting and burdensome tax? (5-4)
6 Arrived with artist on new set for *Claudius*, leaving us source of material to draw on (6,6)
7 Head of agency given first stage of punishment, mostly over mistakes (6)
8 Something to soften medical treatment that hurts! (6)
11 See one north of Paris in a rage – this isn't the best drink (3,9)
15 Global system copes with unusual occurrence here? (9)
16 Unpredictable man taking hold of state (8)
17 Unscrupulous supporter runs into my fielder (8)
19 Early medicine – an incomplete science (6)
20 Coin mostly cast in gold? On the contrary (6)
23 It may appear right, set in ring (5)

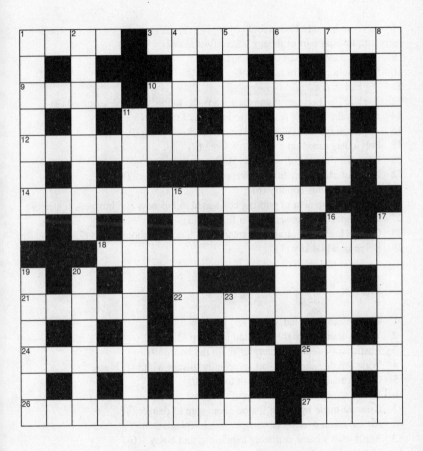

75

ACROSS

1 Account brought back about old soldier (7)
5 Turn up near part of theatre where flier sits (7)
9 Puzzle posed by part of army vehicle (5)
10 Sally holding on for a draw (9)
11 Pig had trapped tail (6)
12 Answer lies between plump and lean – he thinks it's predetermined (8)
14 Wind, rain – who's responsible for a lot of it? (5)
15 An adroit manoeuvre for crossing river down south (9)
18 Previously dined on a pound, or free? (9)
20 Long for time to follow chap (5)
22 One frittering away time by trapping aquatic creature (8)
24 Author pays his country (6)
26 Early development of parking connected to business and business centre (9)
27 Lager specially brewed for Sir Edward (5)
28 Castle Howard's entrance adapted – it's used for school books (7)
29 Beige or white key (7)

DOWN

1 Changes angle of hat, coming to gate (9)
2 Where draughts might be found in a ship (2,5)
3 Rustic work depicting clergyman on the booze (9)
4 Wine – rather ordinary sort, especially to start with (4)
5 Charter man devised for Welsh town (10)
6 Where to see imperial aristocrat's original pal (5)
7 Forecast made by North Briton about sign of danger (7)
8 Article taken over by newspaper – that's plagiarism (5)
13 A girl with a name for being capricious and bossy (10)
16 Coming back on stream (9)
17 Cartel had organised ecclesiastical building (9)
19 Not divulging the queen appearing in old as well as new testament? (2,3,1,1)
21 Peevishness of climber newspaper's shown up (7)
22 Diarist puts last of money into savings plans (5)
23 Date with policeman set up – what about that! (5)
25 Song man heard (4)

ACROSS

1 Retire after defeat, as befits a boxer? (4,4,6)
9 Overact, twirling new sari, greeting Hindu sage (9)
10 English composer's skilful evasion (5)
11 It's audibly granted to listeners (5)
12 Engineers initially find vessel is hard to re-equip (9)
13 Makes out album deserves to be heard (8)
15 Old crone one's taken round good Scottish food (6)
17 Good person replacing centre of 10's cake (6)
19 Husband leaves song about Pooh's friend in vestibule (8)
22 Engage in gambling in army theatre (9)
23 About to pose for further examination (5)
24 Hispanic comrade Vespucci identified without hesitation (5)
25 Cornfield plant an indicator of weather? Nonsense (9)
26 It collapses readily, but Asians make light of it (7,7)

DOWN

1 See poet in my part of London planting tree (8,6)
2 League's accountant shows impatience when driving (7)
3 Prepared for a row, our heartless editor grabs article (5)
4 Treasure in French film about initiator of robbery (8)
5 Who cut short dubious description of decaying matter? (6)
6 Finished a lawsuit – characters starting sentences? (5,4)
7 Favourite Australian river (7)
8 Similarly, say, purchase an identical memento (2,3,4,5)
14 Like a burrowing creature originating on our planet (9)
16 Law enforcers tuck in, not having dined (8)
18 Initially so prolific, showing no originality (7)
20 Like the wind we get from the drink (7)
21 Curious afterthought about universal uproar (6)
23 Note about textile fibre (5)

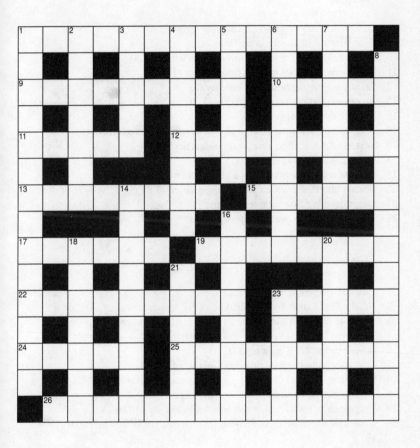

ACROSS

1 Oxford difficult to get into? This may help (8)
5 Poor film subsequently in profit (4,2)
10 Competition that the enemy threatens to win? (4,7,4)
11 The woman without warmth found cover (7)
12 Enemy act almost destroyed old city (7)
13 Be proud, and put up with striking (5,3)
15 Regular time for episode (5)
18 An astronomical time taken by English coming to agreement (5)
20 Was in role in charge, like a school-teacher? (8)
23 Plain dish with gold on edge (7)
25 Dishonest actor appearing as a philosopher (7)
26 Islands all granite with trees looking gnarled (7,8)
27 Dog traversing Somerset terrain (6)
28 Dash into shallow water in the Cape (8)

DOWN

1 Pressure beginning to split lock (6)
2 Band of gold artist fixed around box (9)
3 Listen to all the Commandments being read out and cheer (7)
4 Use force to remove magistrate from hearing (5)
6 It may be the thing required (7)
7 Condescend to be proclaimed as a native of Europe (5)
8 Introduces hospital dept with journalists gathered round (8)
9 An instinctive set of impulses keeps companion lively (8)
14 Traditionalists who may recall what railways used to be like (3,5)
16 Layers of superficial matter from English essayist hiding essential element (9)
17 Leaks? Have a word with servants (8)
19 Army uprising in that place where they're in action? (7)
21 Restrict prisoner? Good! (7)
22 A male in employment, happily occupied (6)
24 A hindrance crossing river brings alarm (5)
25 One who crooned *Love is a Game* (5)

ACROSS

1 Trader chatting in port with seaman (10)
7 Queen gives trick to Yanks (4)
9 Lock without spring allowed illegal entry (8)
10 Clerical sort of mistake at work (6)
11 Did battle turn green to colour of blood? (6)
12 Extrovert, or retiring? (8)
13 Likes to make critical remarks (4)
15 Contest in which comeback's spirited (6,4)
18 Damage got mischief-maker a term in stir (10)
20 Endlessly bitter in this island (4)
21 Pretended to be deeply moved (8)
24 Not at all discreet following denial (6)
26 Work unit backing out of plum contract (6)
27 Weapon that may have brought about armistice out East (8)
28 Spades break up garden soil where tree may be put? (4)
29 Keep firm control (10)

DOWN

2 Basil possibly has cuckoo-pint bordering one plant collection (9)
3 Slacker, nothing less – one who won't succeed (5)
4 You'll hear a slur when he speaks (9)
5 Lavishly spend pounds on a round of drinks (4,3)
6 One sailor catching another up in foreign port (5)
7 With punches and rums sent over and drunk, throws up (9)
8 River runs through fell and swamp (5)
14 Uninspired showing by out-of-form team's stand-off (9)
16 Enter into arrangement regarding holding (9)
17 Steam air dispersed left a wispy cloud (5,4)
19 Customer's tip sure to be shared out (3-4)
22 Canary Island's fine at first (5)
23 Right is shortly to be announced to supply this garment (5)
25 Cut up about soldier coming over? Consider carefully (5)

ACROSS

1 Play *The Trout*, to amuse (6)
4 On Christmas tree, put conventional dressing (5,3)
10 Contrite tear about empty pledge taken with a testament (9)
11 Why phone doesn't ring, we hear, for prizegiver? (5)
12 Drink for which Scott's wasted pounds? (5)
13 Crimson-clad emissary not given precedence (9)
14 Admirer getting over feature of King's chapel (3,8)
16 In game, dropped by cover (3)
18 Withdrawing objection to some ice-cream (3)
20 Draftee once ordered into this American army (11)
22 Inflamed, being second in race, strongly fancied to win (9)
23 Resonant sound from family grand (5)
24 An indifferent philosopher (5)
25 Witch-doctor happy to have cloud over his reputation? (9)
26 Cows almost always returning to exotic plant (8)
27 Down for one charge, with number to be worked out (6)

DOWN

1 Rage, maybe giving it what-for (5,1,3)
2 Toy explosive charge boy had in revolver (7)
3 Left extraordinary person, one hating company (5)
5 Bright bunch working for TV hearing news as it breaks (14)
6 Announced wrong-doing expectantly to religious assembly (9)
7 Controller arrives, having eaten a little something (7)
8 Given modest share of grief, died (5)
9 Earl had laundry ruined by clownish performers (6,3,5)
15 Like a piece of Beethoven's, teasing with double stopping entry for cello (9)
17 Depression over bishop appearing in jolly headgear (9)
19 So dispense with candlelight for the banquet? (4-3)
21 Oh dear, can we hear an American statesman? (7)
22 Educated person found Latin so vital (5)
23 Small role in relief work (5)

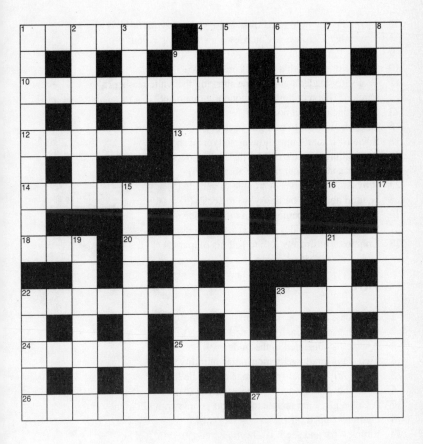

ACROSS

1 I would come in to bowl over, but I've lost my partner (5)
4 November 11th, when Chuzzlewit's embracing parent (9)
9 What's left without a souvenir? (9)
10 Tongue or fish with a dash of oregano (5)
11 Feel sorry leader's gone – one showing the white feather (5)
12 Quote: "This requires no orthodontic treatment" (5,4)
13 State touchy about poem (7)
15 One who is slow to pull girl back (7)
18 Socialist leader – one showing untypical shock? (7)
20 Storytelling enthrals child – that's an understatement (7)
21 Sapper and irregular may be abrasive (9)
23 Provide for extremes of trouble in vehicle (5)
25 Natural ability to be flashy, so to speak (5)
26 Welcoming competition, ready to explode (4-5)
27 Sailors in two shades of blue (5,4)
28 Composer ultimately loth to sell his output (5)

DOWN

1 Bird soars above trees shattered in battle (9)
2 Object reserved finally disposed of (5)
3 A wine list amended in the middle (9)
4 Two ways unknown demonstrates humility (7)
5 In *The Mirror*, quality coverage for whale (7)
6 I had shown the way to be unemployed (5)
7 As a beggar, I am unable to support people with old money (9)
8 Garment ripped off (5)
14 Sitting – try and see if it's been altered (9)
16 State investigator ill-advised to intrude (9)
17 Refuse to believe record – colour it (9)
19 Go down and see scholar displaying his achievement (7)
20 Gallery rearranged, to a great extent (7)
21 Seat that has gone to the right until now (2,3)
22 Beautiful girl left in danger (5)
24 The language of soldiers joining very small unit (5)

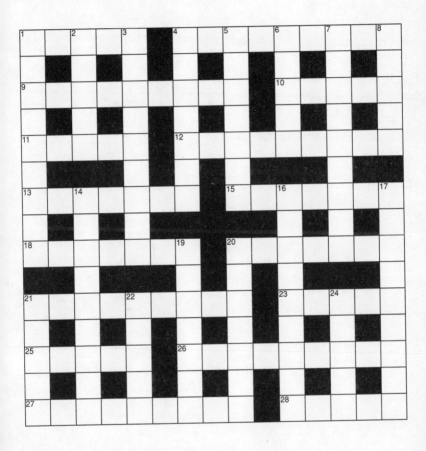

THE SOLUTIONS

SOLUTIONS

1

H	A	D	E	S		H	E	R	M	I	T	A	G	E
A		E		H		O		E		N		L		V
R	E	L	I	E	F	M	A	P		S	A	B	R	E
O		F		L		E		O		T		A		R
O	U	T	F	L	Y		P	R	I	E	S	T	L	Y
W			A		P		T		A		R			N
O	B	J	E	C	T	I	V	E		D	U	O	M	O
N		U		G		D				S		W		
T	A	S	T	E		M	E	L	A	N	E	S	I	A
H		T		A		E		Y		O				N
E	M	I	G	R	A	N	T		I	S	L	A	N	D
H		F		L		T		S		E		L		T
I	L	I	A	D		A	U	T	O	G	R	A	P	H
L		E		O		R		I		A		C		E
L	O	R	D	M	A	Y	O	R		Y	U	K	O	N

2

L	O	C	K	K	E	E	P	E	R		C	L	E	F
O		A		N		M		G			L			I
P	E	R	F	O	R	A	T	O	R		P	A	I	R
E		O		W		C		I		B		N		S
	B	U	S	T		I	N	S	O	L	V	E	N	T
S		S		H		A		T		A		R		C
P	R	E	T	E	X	T	S		S	C	H	O	O	L
A		R		E		H		K			A			A
C	O	M	M	O	N		T	A	D	P	O	L	E	S
E		A		P		E		R		U		O		S
W	E	S	T	E	R	N	E	R		D	A	B	S	
O		C		S		M		I		D		E		A
M	O	A	N		W	E	E	D	K	I	L	L	E	R
A		R		S		A		N		I		I		C
N	O	A	H		C	H	I	N	A	G	R	A	P	H

3

4

172

5

6

7

8

SOLUTIONS

9

10

11

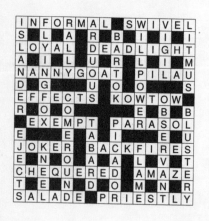

12

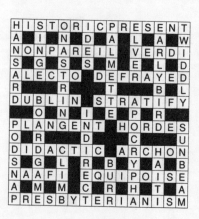

13

14

15

16

SOLUTIONS

17

18

19

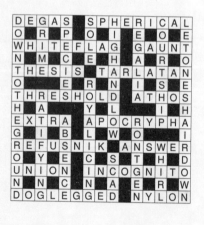

20

21

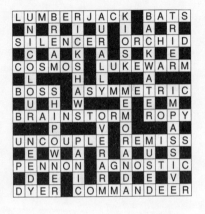

22

23

24

SOLUTIONS

25

26

27

28

29

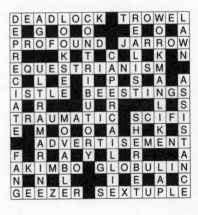

30

31

32

SOLUTIONS

33

L	E	E	D	S			T	O	S	C	A	N	I	N	I
A		D		H		U		E		R		G			N
T	R	I	M	E	S	T	E	R		C	R	U	S	T	
E		C		A		U		P		L		A			H
R	O	T	A	T	E		D	E	T	A	I	N	E	E	
A			H		R		N		M		O				L
L	A	R	C	E	N	I	S	T		P	O	D	I	A	
T		E			N		I					O			S
H	O	S	T	A		G	I	N	G	E	R	N	U	T	
I		E		S		L		E		C					R
N	I	N	E	T	I	E	S		P	H	R	A	S	E	
K		T		A		A		T		O		R			S
I	N	F	E	R		D	E	R	R	I	N	G	D	O	
N		U		E			A			N		U			R
G	O	L	D	E	N	R	O	D		G	R	E	A	T	

34

T	O	R	C	H	L	I	G	H	T			C	O	M	B
	D		L		I		O		O		O			E	
A	D	M	I	T	T	E	D		K	I	M	O	N	O	
	J		N		T		S		A		E		S		
B	O	O	K	I	E		L	A	Y	W	O	M	A	N	
	B				R		O				F				
A	M	O	S		B	O	T	T	L	E	F	E	E	D	
	A		A		I			O			I		N		
O	N	E	M	A	N	S	H	O	W		T	U	P	I	
			A			A		E					A		
C	H	A	R	I	S	M	A		S	C	H	I	S	M	
	E		K		H		R		T		A		S		
V	I	R	A	G	O		L	E	O	N	I	D	A	S	
	S		N		A		E		F		K		N		
S	T	U	D		L	E	M	O	T	J	U	S	T	E	

35

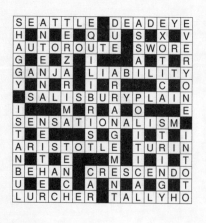

S	E	A	T	T	L	E		D	E	A	D	E	Y	E
H		N		E		Q		U		S		X		V
A	U	T	O	R	O	U	T	E		S	W	O	R	E
G		E		Z		I				A		T		R
G	A	N	J	A		L	I	A	B	I	L	I	T	Y
Y		N		R		I		R		C				O
	S	A	L	I	S	B	U	R	Y	P	L	A	I	N
I		M		R		A		O						E
S	E	N	S	A	T	I	O	N	A	L	I	S	M	
T		E		S		G		I		T		I		I
A	R	I	S	T	O	T	L	E		T	U	R	I	N
N		T		E			M		I			I		T
B	E	H	A	N		C	R	E	S	C	E	N	D	O
U		E		C		A		N		A		G		T
L	U	R	C	H	E	R		T	A	L	L	Y	H	O

36

N	E	T	T	L	E	R	A	S	H		B	E	A	K
	S		Y		N		L		O		R		T	
S	C	A	R	C	I	T	Y		U	N	I	A	T	E
	A		O		G		S		N		C		I	
S	L	A	L	O	M		S	I	D	E	K	I	C	K
	A				A		U				B			
E	T	N	A		T	E	M	P	O	R	A	L	L	Y
	O		U		I			Y		T		A		
E	R	A	D	I	C	A	T	E	S		S	I	N	E
	I				E		T					D		
B	E	H	O	L	D	E	N		E	N	G	A	G	E
	L		T		Y		D		R		R		R	
S	A	L	A	M	I		R	U	B	R	I	C	A	L
	N		P		N		I		E		E		V	
A	D	Z	E		G	O	L	D	D	I	G	G	E	R

180

37

```
Y O R I C K ▪ S P R I T Z E R
▪ P ▪ M ▪ A ▪ E ▪ I ▪ R ▪ V ▪
P E N I C I L L I N ▪ E S A U
▪ R ▪ T ▪ S ▪ F ▪ G ▪ S ▪ P ▪
J A P A N E S E ▪ W I S D O M
▪ ▪ T ▪ R ▪ X ▪ O ▪ ▪ R ▪
T H A I ▪ ▪ P A R T I S A N
▪ O ▪ V ▪ S ▪ L ▪ M ▪ N ▪ T
S W E E T P E A ▪ ▪ T E E M
▪ A ▪ ▪ A ▪ N ▪ C ▪ E ▪
B R I D A L ▪ A Q U A R I U M
▪ E ▪ A ▪ P ▪ T ▪ T ▪ V ▪ S
D Y E R ▪ E C O L O G I C A L
▪ O ▪ C ▪ E ▪ R ▪ F ▪ E ▪ G
B U O Y A N C Y ▪ F A W L E Y
```

38

```
F L O S S ▪ S Q U A R E C U T
O ▪ F ▪ C ▪ P ▪ S ▪ E ▪ A ▪ I
R E F U R N I S H ▪ M O P E D
C ▪ ▪ A ▪ R ▪ E ▪ O ▪ T ▪ Y
E X E M P L I G R A T I A ▪
R ▪ I ▪ E ▪ T ▪ ▪ E ▪ I ▪ C
T O F F ▪ O U T T O L U N C H
A ▪ F ▪ L ▪ A ▪ I ▪ Y ▪ H ▪ E
I N E Q U A L I T Y ▪ F O U R
N ▪ L ▪ C ▪ ▪ L ▪ W ▪ O ▪ R
▪ T A K E T H E M I C K E Y
T ▪ O ▪ Y ▪ E ▪ P ▪ L ▪ ▪ P
H E W E D ▪ S C A R L A T T I
A ▪ E ▪ I ▪ T ▪ G ▪ O ▪ E ▪ C
W O R K P L A C E ▪ W H A C K
```

39

40

SOLUTIONS

41

```
P A R A D I S E L O S T
I   E   R P   E   O   B U
Q U A K E R I S M   A G A I N
U   C   A   N   O V   S   T
A T H O M E   I N F E R I O R
N       B     A     L     U
T A R P O N   A D E L A I D E
  I   A   P   E     E   S
F U N C T I O N   S T O K E S
A   G     P       H       U
C A P S I C U M   M A D C A P
A   U   N   L   C   R   H   R
D E L O S   A L O N G S I D E
E   L   E   C   W   I   N   M
    S T E E P L E C H A S E
```

42

```
F O O T S L O G     M   F   O
  S   H   I     E S C A L L O P
S T O U T E S T     R   A   E
  I   R   G     S P E C I M E N
A N T I H E R O     H   I   P
  A   B   M     M A T E R N A L
  T   L   A   E     S   G   A
C O M E I N T O O N E S O W N
R   A   M   N     I   E   H
A L L S P I C E     T   I   E
C   I   E     S T R I C K E N
K I N D L I N G     O   E   Z
P   G   L     O R G A N D I E
O P E R E T T A     E   T   E
T   R   D     T A N D O O R I
```

43

```
T H R E E M E N I N A B O A T
E   I   X   A   N   S   V   R
A P P R A I S E S   S I E N A
R   O   C   T   P   E   R   I
S O N A T A   B I A T H L O N
U   I       R       A   E
P I G E O N   L E I S U R E D
    E   N   F   D   A   G
M I N I S T R Y   E N N E A D
A   U   E       D       E
L I F E P E E R   A B U L I A
L   L   I   F   M   A   Y   R
A L E R T   A R A I N Y D A Y
R   C   C   L   I   K   I   M
D U T C H E L M D I S E A S E
```

44

```
  S T I C K O U T A M I L E
  T   C   I   P   G   N   G
W A F T   N A T A L   T O G A
  G   U   K   I   O   E   A
B E E S W I N G   W I R I N G
  D   N   H       B   D
W I N C H E S T E R   R A S H
  R   O   S       E   E   P
F E R N   S P O T T E D D O G
  C   T   B   A       O
S T A R C H   S H I L L I N G
  I   A   A   C   L   I   R
T O I L   S O U S E   M O A N
  N   T   T   R   R   B   C
  S M O K E L E S S Z O N E
```

45

```
H B O M B   U N D R E S S E D
Y   V   R   N   O   A   K   R
P R O K O F I E V   R H Y M E
O   I   I   S   E   N   R   A
M I D D L E O F T H E R O A D
A   E   N   A   S   C
N A T U R E   M I S T A K E N
I   A   M   L       E   O
A B I N G D O N   I S A T I N
  L   A   O   E   Y       P
S O L A R P R O M I N E N C E
T   I   O   L   B   O   E   R
A R G O T   A I L A N T H U S
I   H   T   N   E   Y   R   O
R O T T E R D A M   M O U R N
```

46

```
S C E N I C   C A M O M I L E
  I   E   O   O   O   A   O
F L O O D W A T E R   N O O K
  I   L   P   T   T   O   S
P A N O R A M A   G A R D E N
    G   T   G   A     L
G O B I     E I G H T E E N
  T   S   S   I   E   U   A
C H A M P I O N     N A F F
  E     G   D   A   E
O R I G I N   U P L I F T E D
W   R   P   S   L     U   V
S I L O   O U T F I E L D E R
  S   O   S   R   E   L   N
G E O M E T R Y   D R Y I S H
```

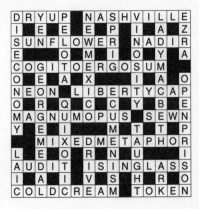

47

```
M U C H N E S S   B E H E A D
O   R   E   P   A   E   B
N O I S E M A K E R   A C R E
I   C   D   R   C   R   I
T A K E F O R G R A N T E D
O   E   U   E   R   E   G
R A T T L E D   B O U N C E R
  E   N       L   O
H I R S U T E   S E I S M I C
  M   C   E   C   C   P   I
  A U R O R A B O R E A L I S
  G   A   T   O   B   I   T
P I N T   A L L T H E S A M E
  N   C   I   E   R   N   R
P E A H E N   B R I G H T E N
```

48

```
D R Y U P   N A S H V I L L E
I   E   E   E   P   I   A   Z
S U N F L O W E R   N A D I R
E     O   M   I   O   Y   A
C O G I T O E R G O S U M
O   E   A   X     I   A   O
N E O N   L I B E R T Y C A P
O   R   Q   C   C   Y   B   E
M A G N U M O P U S   S E W N
Y   E   I     M   T   T   P
  M I X E D M E T A P H O R
L   E   O   R   N   U     I
A U D I T   I S I N G L A S S
I   A   I   V   S   H   R   O
C O L D C R E A M   T O K E N
```

SOLUTIONS

49

```
B R A Y   S P E L L B O U N D
I   V     A   A   R   N   E
G L E N   I N U N D A T I O N
A   R   P   D   G   I   S   I
M U S C O V A D O   N I O B E
I   I   S       U   W   N   R
S H O O T I N G S T A R
T   N   P   E   T   S   E   A
      D O U B L E W H A M M Y
L   A   S   R       I   P   R
I A M B I   A L B A N I A N S
M   E   T   S   A   G   T   H
P E R N I C K E T Y   T H A I
E   C   V   A   H       I   R
T H E R E U N D E R   A C R E
```

50

```
F A R T H I N G A L E S
I   E   I   A   E   A   T   F
N E A R T H I N G   S T A L L
A   L   W   L   R   E   M   E
G A M B I T   B O L D F A C E
L   C       T       R   C
E U R E K A   S A N G U I N E
    A   E   N   T   R   N
B E G E T T E R   H O L D U P
E   T       W       U       U
R E R E M I C E   A N G L E R
B   A   A   O   O   D   E   I
E N D E D   M A R C H P A S T
R   E   A   E   A   O   V   A
        E M E R A L D G R E E N
```

51

```
E N G U L F   C O C K C R O W
  I   P   I   O   I   O   I
E G G S H E L L   S T A S I S
  H   T   L   L   C   E   H
S T R A D D L E   T H E M O B
  J   I   F   C   E   A   O
  A   R E A C T I O N   R   N
A R M S   R   O   W   B Y R E
S   A   P E T R O N E L   A
T   R   R   S   E   O   T
E L I C I T   P O R P O I S E
R   G   M   I   S   D   T
I S O B A R   E T H E R E A L
S   L   T   C   I   E   I
K E D G E R E E   P A D D L E
```

52

```
S E L F P O R T R A I T
I   I   E   E   O   L   C   A
N O V A E   P E T T I C O A T
K   E   R   E   A   A   A   T
I N D I G N A N T   D E L T A
N       R   T   I       P   C
G I B B O N   S O N G B O O K
    R   U   P   N   U   R
F L A G P O L E   B I G T O P
I   C   A   H   N       N   A
A S K E W   T R A V E R S E D
S   E   E   O   W   A   U   D
C A T A L O N I A   P E S T O
O   S   S   I   I   I   H   C
        S H O C K I N G P I N K
```

184

53

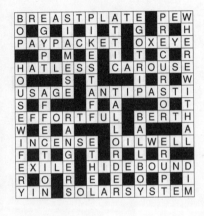

54

55

56

SOLUTIONS

57

B	O	O	B		P	A	S	S	E	D	P	A	W	N
A		R			M		C		R		S		O	
L	A	D	Y		H	A	I	R	R	A	I	S	E	R
D		I		C		T		A		U		U		W
P	A	N	T	H	E	I	S	M		G	A	M	M	A
A		A		A				B		H		E		Y
T	A	R	A	M	A	S	A	L	A	T	A			
E		Y		B		I		E		B		D		C
			B	E	G	G	A	R	S	O	P	E	R	A
S		B		R		H		A		A		L		S
A	X	I	O	M		T	A	M	E	R	L	A	N	E
N		S		U		R		A		D		M		B
D	R	E	S	S	S	E	N	S	E		K	A	Y	O
R		C		I		A		O		R		R		O
A	N	T	E	C	E	D	E	N	T		P	E	A	K

58

R	A	P	I	E	R		I	N	U	N	D	A	T	E
E		O		Y		M		A		O		S		R
C	R	U	D	E	L	Y		V	E	N	I	S	O	N
U		N		C		N		I		E		A		S
M	O	C	K	O	R	A	N	G	E		G	U	S	T
B		E		N		A		H		L				
E	I	D	E	T	I	C		T	O	A	S	T	E	R
N				A		O		O		L				E
T	O	P	I	C	A	L		R	I	F	L	I	N	G
		O		T		L		N		S				R
F	U	M	E		D	O	U	B	L	E	T	I	M	E
I		A		B		T		A		L		D		T
L	I	T	U	R	G	Y		C	A	S	T	O	F	F
E		U		A		P		K		O		R		U
D	O	M	I	N	O	E	S		U	N	R	E	A	L

59

M	U	R	M	U	R		H	A	N	D	M	A	I	D
	N		A		I		E		A		P		E	
C	R	A	C	K	N	E	L		S	T	E	R	N	A
	I		A		G		I		E		E		D	
	P		R		S		C	O	M	P	O	S	E	R
S	E	N	O	R	I	T	A		A		S			I
E			N		D		L		L		K			N
E	X	C	I	T	E	D		L	A	M	B	I	N	G
R		R		H		S		N		R				E
S		O		R		C	O	N	S	I	D	E	R	
U	N	S	E	E	M	L	Y		U		G		M	
C		S		S			T		A		H		E	
K	N	I	G	H	T		H	A	L	F	T	E	R	M
E		N		E			E		L		O		G	
R	I	G	O	R	O	U	S		Y	O	N	D	E	R

60

W	I	N	D	L	A	S	S		S	M	O	O	T	H
R		E		U		A		S		A		R		O
E	X	C	E	L		R	O	U	N	D	E	L	A	Y
S		T		U		C		P		H		O		D
T	R	A	N	S	L	A	T	E		A	P	P	L	E
L		R		S		R		T		T				N
E	P	I	G	R	A	M		B	U	T	T	O	N	
R		N		O				E			S		S	S
	P	E	L	M	E	T		S	C	R	A	T	C	H
S		A		U		C			R		R	
H	U	M	A	N		P	R	O	S	T	R	A	T	E
R		O		M		T		R		C		D	
A	S	T	R	O	N	A	U	T		I	L	I	A	D
N		E		S		N		I		A		S		E
K	I	T	T	E	N		H	E	A	D	G	E	A	R

186

61

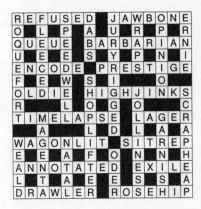

62

63

64

SOLUTIONS

65

66

TAKETHEFLOOR
SCOUR GONEGOOSE
UPTHEPOLE NYALA
OPTION MISTRIAL
SHORTCUT PAUNCH
RUSTY EXTENSION
PARAMATTA OREAD
ANARMANDALEG

MEDUSA DECREPIT
BARB BOOTLICKER
GODWIT IMMERSES
TRADESMAN AMATI
NONET GATHERING
PATHETIC NOTION
NOTSODUSTY NAIL
REDEEMER DRACHM

67

68

MAGOG CHARTISTS
DISPELLED HACEK
GOODSAMARITAN
SOLE FIRERAISER
ATTHEREADY OGRE
ROLLERCOASTER
POTTO INITIATED
VIDEOTAPE SPEAR

ROSSETTI ACCEPT
BEDOFROSES WAIF
CENTRESPREAD
HOME MAINSTAY
BACKDOWN AXIS
CONCERTPITCH
STUB GUNSLINGER
WANTAD LASVEGAS

69

D	O	R	I	A	N	G	R	A	Y		M	A	C	E
	S		N		I		A		E		O		O	
E	T	R	U	S	C	A	N		A	B	O	A	R	D
	E		R	K	S		T		N		G			
K	O	R	E	A	N		A	S	S	A	S	S	I	N
	P		A		C				H					
J	A	V	A		M	A	K	E	W	E	I	G	H	T
	T		L		E			A		N		O		
P	H	I	L	O	S	O	P	H	Y		E	A	T	S
	O			A		Z			P					
B	L	O	W	O	V	E	R		G	A	M	B	O	L
E		A		I		V		O		I		T		
W	A	G	N	E	R		E	G	O	I	D	E	A	L
	F		C		U		N		S		G		T	
H	Y	D	E		S	Q	U	E	E	Z	E	B	O	X

70

L	O	B	E	L	I	A		T	A	P	R	O	O	M
I		A		O		T		E		A		W		A
T	I	G	H	T		T	I	N	O	P	E	N	E	R
O		A		T		R		E		E		E		I
T	A	T	T	O	O	I	S	T		R	A	D	O	N
E		E				B		C				C		E
S	A	L	O	P		U	P	H	O	L	S	T	E	R
		L		U		T		O		I		E		
O	V	E	R	S	P	E	N	T		P	O	S	E	S
F		H		H				H				T		L
F	R	A	N	C		B	R	E	A	D	L	I	N	E
S		N		H		I		A		E		F		N
I	N	G	R	A	I	N	E	D		N	A	I	A	D
D		E		G				E		I		E		E
E	N	L	A	R	G	E		D	E	M	U	R	E	R

71

S	P	R	Y		A	R	C	H	I	M	E	D	E	S
W		U			E		E		O		E		T	
A	N	N	A		G	R	E	A	T	U	N	C	L	E
L		A		D		A		D		N		A		L
L	A	M	P	O	O	N	E	D		T	A	M	I	L
O			I		T			R		A		P		A
W	E	L	S	H	R	A	R	E	B	I	T			
S		E		E		L		S		N		D		S
			T	H	E	L	A	S	T	S	T	R	A	W
H		S		O		I			I		U		A	
A	C	T	I	N		G	U	A	R	D	S	M	A	N
M		I		O		A		D		E		R		S
M	A	N	S	U	E	T	U	D	E		L	O	C	O
E		G		R		O		L			L		N	
R	O	O	D	S	C	R	E	E	N		F	L	O	G

72

A	B	S	T	A	I	N		S	P	A	N	G	L	E
U		I		S		O		O		U		R		N
T	O	N	G	S		S	A	L	A	D	D	A	Y	S
O		E		O		H		A		E		N		U
M	E	D	I	C	I		I	R	O	N	W	A	R	E
A		I		I		S	P		P			D		
T	H	E	T	A		C	H	O	C	O	L	A	T	E
I			T			H		W		R				A
C	A	S	S	E	R	O	L	E		C	H	A	I	R
		U				O		R		H		U		N
S	U	R	T	I	T	L	E		D	E	A	R	M	E
A		V		B		R		P		S		E		S
M	A	I	D	S	T	O	N	E		T	R	A	I	T
O		V		E		O		L		R		T		L
S	T	E	R	N	U	M		T	R	A	G	E	D	Y

SOLUTIONS

73

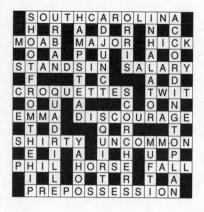

74

75

76

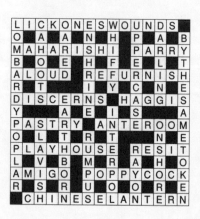

SOLUTIONS

77

```
S H O E H O R N ■ H A R D U P
T ■ R ■ E ■ E ■ A ■ R ■ E ■ R
R A C E A G A I N S T T I M E
E ■ H ■ R ■ V ■ I ■ I ■ G ■ S
S H E A T H E ■ M Y C E N A E
S ■ S ■ E ■ ■ A ■ L ■ ■ ■ N
■ S T A N D O U T ■ E V E N T
S ■ R ■ ■ L ■ E ■ ■ ■ P ■ S
E P A C T ■ D I D A C T I C ■
E ■ ■ ■ H ■ G ■ ■ O ■ T ■ A
P L A T E A U ■ B E N T H A M
A ■ L ■ A ■ A ■ I ■ F ■ E ■ U
G R E A T E R A N T I L L E S
E ■ R ■ R ■ D ■ G ■ N ■ I ■ E
S E T T E R ■ F O R E L A N D
```

78

```
W H O L E S A L E R ■ D I D O
■ E ■ O ■ L ■ A ■ A ■ I ■ R
T R E S P A S S ■ B I S H O P
■ B ■ E ■ N ■ H ■ A ■ G ■ W
W A R R E D ■ O U T G O I N G
■ R ■ ■ E ■ U ■ ■ R ■ ■ ■
D I G S ■ R E T U R N G A M E
■ U ■ T ■ E ■ ■ E ■ E ■ A
I M P A I R M E N T ■ S A R K
■ ■ L ■ ■ N ■ E ■ ■ ■ E
A F F E C T E D ■ N O W I S E
■ I ■ M ■ R ■ U ■ T ■ E ■ T
E N G A G E ■ S C I M I T A R
■ C ■ T ■ W ■ E ■ O ■ G ■ I
S H O E ■ S T R O N G H O L D
```

79

```
T I C K L E ■ F I R S T A I D
H ■ A ■ O ■ L ■ N ■ Y ■ R ■ O
R E P E N T A N T ■ N O B E L
O ■ S ■ E ■ U ■ E ■ A ■ I ■ E
W A T E R ■ R E L E G A T E D
A ■ A ■ ■ E ■ L ■ O ■ E ■
F A N V A U L T I N G ■ R U G
I ■ ■ R ■ A ■ G ■ U ■ ■ L
T U B ■ C O N F E D E R A T E
■ ■ L ■ H ■ D ■ N ■ L ■ N
B L O O D S H O T ■ C L A N G
A ■ W ■ U ■ A ■ S ■ A ■ S ■ A
S T O I C ■ R A I N M A K E R
I ■ U ■ A ■ D ■ A ■ E ■ A ■ R
C A T T L E Y A ■ C O U N T Y
```

80

```
W I D O W ■ M A R T I N M A S
O ■ E ■ A ■ O ■ O ■ D ■ E ■ T
O R E M A I N D E R ■ L I N G O
C ■ U ■ S ■ E ■ Q ■ E ■ D ■ L
E G R E T ■ S O U N D B I T E
S ■ ■ L ■ T ■ A ■ ■ C ■
T E S T I F Y ■ L A G G A R D
E ■ E ■ N ■ ■ A ■ N ■ I
R E D H E A D ■ L I T O T E S
■ E ■ ■ I ■ A ■ E ■ ■ C
S A N D P A P E R ■ C A T E R
O ■ T ■ E ■ L ■ G ■ R ■ A ■ E
F L A I R ■ O P E N A R M E D
A ■ R ■ I ■ M ■ L ■ S ■ I ■ I
R O Y A L N A V Y ■ H O L S T
```

Other *Times*
crossword publications

The Times Crossword Book 1
ISBN 0-00-710833-8   £5.99

The Times Crossword Book 2
ISBN 0-00-711581-4   £5.99

The Times Crossword Book 3
ISBN 0-00-712195-4   £5.99

The Times Crossword Book 4
ISBN 0-00-712674-3   £5.99

The Times Crossword Book 6
ISBN 0-00-714626-4   £5.99

The Times Crossword Book 7
ISBN 0-00-716538-2   £5.99

The Times Jumbo Cryptic Crossword Book 1
ISBN 0-00-714715-5   £6.99

The Times Jumbo Cryptic Crossword Book 2
ISBN 0-00-714630-2   £6.99

The Times Jumbo Cryptic Crossword Book 3
ISBN 0-00-714481-4   £6.99

The Times Jumbo Cryptic Crossword Book 4
ISBN 0-00-712751-0   £6.99

How To Do The Times Crossword
ISBN 0-00-710840-0   £5.99